DUSK AND DAWN
IN VILLAGE INDIA

DUSK AND DAWN
IN VILLAGE INDIA

Zahir Ahmed

FREDERICK A. PRAEGER, Publishers
New York · Washington · London

FREDERICK A PRAEGER, Publishers
111 Fourth Avenue, New York 3, N.Y., U.S.A.
77-79 Charlotte Street, London W.1, England

Published in the United States of America in 1966
by Frederick A. Praeger, Inc., Publishers

Library of Congress Catalog Card Number: 66-11565

Printed in Great Britain

CONTENTS

PREFACE

Guy Wint

SINCE it became independent, India has been restlessly engaged upon an analysis of its changing social order and of the ups and downs of its economy. These efforts have resulted in a large output of literature, and this has been supplemented by the publications of foreigners, especially Americans. The facts of land tenure have been laid bare; the statistics of untouchability have been worked over; the woes of the village schoolmaster have been recorded and the tyranny of the Patel and Deshmukh has been exposed; the shifting class structure has been set down in endless tables showing what has happened to the real wealth of the various classes which make up India's 450 million people.

With all this information to hand, India ought to be more real as a country than ever before. But it is hard to feel emotion over a statistic, and, in the great effusion of intellectual effort, India and Indian social life have shrunk and withered, and have become unreal.

The great value of this book is that it reverses this tendency and presents Indians as a living people. Without any original research, and especially without statistical fortification, Mr Zahir Ahmed has shown what life was really like in India during the two decades with which it deals, away from all the plans of Government and the categories imposed on the people. The India which the narrative surveys is the real India, the down-to-earth India, and it is India as it appears, not to one gifted with the eye of faith, but to the realist, cautious, and modestly idealist administrator; above all, to the professional administrator whose training has equipped him for observing realities in the village, not for seeing visions in blue books.

And it is from such a class of professionals that Mr Zahir Ahmed himself comes. The formative years of his life were passed in the service of Hyderabad State. The description of one of the figures in this book might, with certain variations, have been used of him:

> He was neither a nobleman nor a feudal lord when he entered Government Service; he was only one of the middle class. But once in service he brought to life an air of superiority and exclusiveness. He felt a passionate loyalty to the state of Hyderabad. He was very efficient; he kept his whole jurisdiction under his thumb and was immensely popular. His sense of loyalty could tolerate nothing opposed to the welfare of the Raj but the welfare of the Raj was to him really the welfare of the people.

He is a Moslem of Hyderabad, and this means that he is a little more soaked in the Indian tradition than a Moslem of the Punjab could be. The Hindu world is more present to him, and the world of the Middle East, of Persia and the Arabs, is a little farther away. Yet even so, few people would challenge that the Moslem outlook in Hyderabad is as clear-sighted as anywhere else in Moslem India.

I first met Mr Zahir Ahmed twenty years ago when he was working on Hyderabad affairs in London. His position was delicate and embarrassing. At this time he was Hyderabad's Secretary for Foreign Affairs, and was closely associated with Sir Walter Monckton, who was negotiating for the Nizam of Hyderabad with the Government of India. It was at this time that Jawaharlal Nehru came to know of Zahir Ahmed's abilities and attitudes.

Mr Nehru intervened, and when Hyderabad collapsed in September 1948 he appointed Zahir Ahmed to look after the winding up of Hyderabad's affairs in London. It was a difficult task, and it says much that his work was commended alike by the Nizam and by the Government of India. Since that time Ahmed has held a high position in the United Nations Secretariat. From this point of vantage he has been able to watch the unfolding policies of India. Aloofness has made his view more penetrating.

This book is a panorama of the life of India. It deals with the life of all the types of Indian society, and with their advancement or adversities over twenty years. The reader must not expect to find real people. The book is not a novel: it is a meeting ground of ideas. The people who throng its pages do not exactly take on real flesh and blood, like the men and women on Kim's 'Grand Trunk Road'; but they are vital shadows who proclaim what they are and shout aloud all the problems and the political considerations of India.

Such is *Dusk and Dawn in Village India*. From it, I am confident that more is to be learned about the problems and atmosphere of India than from all the official studies and the economists' reports. And so I give way to the text of a most pregnant study.

*Reverently dedicated
to the memory of
Jawaharlal Nehru
who, out of his great
understanding, gave
encouragement and inspiration
in the writing of this account
of one corner of the land he loved*

PROLOGUE

FOR more than four hours I had been turning over the mass of manuscripts bequeathed to me by my old friend—let us call him Mohammad Rihaz. I sat back and thought first of the man who was no more, and then of the papers and notes scattered around me on the floor. I ran over in my mind the events recalled in these documents that Rihaz had sent me for safe keeping just a month before he died in the distant country in which he had chosen to live after retirement.

I had known that I would be his literary executor. Perhaps because we had been the dearest of friends and close associates in Government Service and had shared the confidences which only young men communicate to each other, I had found myself reluctant to examine his papers. Unwrapping them somehow seemed almost sacrilegious, as if it meant disinterring the remains of a man who was alive and breathing only a few weeks ago.

I had sat on the floor for quite a while in hesitation before I started on the tightly wrapped bundle which carried in his own execrable scrawl the bold legend, 'Notes for my book'. I recalled his last letter to me in which he had said: 'As for my notes, you may publish them, burn them or use the damned things for wrapping up your boots. I shall not care, and I shall be beyond the reach of libel actions and the Government Servants' Conduct Rules.'

Just like Rihaz to refer so contemptuously to work which was really dear to his heart! It reminded me of the incident when, on school speech-day, the Headmaster had called him to the platform to receive the four highest awards. Rihaz had casually dropped the medals into his pocket and had refused to read the citations! I recalled another incident. He had been promoted to a high post in a District and when the rest of us congratulated him, he had remarked airily that the job only looked big—any fool could handle it as well!

In the days that followed, however, I pulled myself together and selected a small portion of his notes from the hillock of manuscripts. Some of the notes ran into lengthy narrative accounts. Some appeared to be quotations. I am, however, letting them speak for him. I have only tried to put them in some order in the hope that they will convey to the reader, in a coherent fashion, something of those exciting experiences which made up his life. It was fitting that he should have finished this massive labour just before setting out on what was to be his final visit to the villages in which he was working before he retired from the service.

His personality represented some of the strangest extremes I have found in any of my friends. He came of a land-owning family, and while there was enough money for all his needs, and some perhaps for the luxuries of life, he had always lived simply and without ostentation. For generations his people had been on the side of law and order. They were traditionalists; not so Rihaz. He could best be described, I believe, as an aristocratic radical. His conservative background was responsible, no doubt, for these dominant characteristics in his personality. Yet this was the man who, much earlier than the rest of us, had heard a deep voice constantly urging him to give his thought, time and money to the destitute whenever he came across them. This he did secretly, silently, in his own way.

As I think of him, I know now as I knew then that it was neither routine duty, nor ambition, nor a desire to impress his superiors with his abilities, which had prompted his constant excursions deep into the countryside. It was love, nothing but love, which impelled him. Yes, love for those miserable, maddening village folk, love for the unkempt little children who clamoured round him, love even for the corrupt, inefficient and shamefully underpaid officials, love for his own India that inspired him in his labours throughout his life.

Nothing was too much trouble for Durragaru, 'sir' or 'master', no village too far away to be visited, no argument between farmers over a couple of pounds of grain too petty to be heard. When he had first gone into the remote areas of the State to work with these people, they were puzzled by his abrupt manner and, at times, by his harsh words: they did not know what to expect of him. Later on, when these simple people learnt to know him, they welcomed him as only a grateful villager can welcome a benefactor. His visits then became occasions for rejoicing and merriment.

Sincerity and compassion, the two great qualities which underlay everything he did, were disguised at times in a peculiar way by his brittle temper and, strangely enough, by his lack of humour. On some occasions Rihaz did indeed enjoy a joke; on others, even the most laughable situations left him cold. They made him withdraw, as it were, into his shell. A short temper and a humourless approach made him at times no easy colleague. More often than he realised, they were the cause of the difficulties which he found in working with his superiors.

These difficulties became particularly pronounced whenever he was called upon to carry through a programme based upon a policy to which he could not whole-heartedly subscribe. As time moved on and projects, programmes and plans were drawn up, his disagreements with those officials and ministers to whom he was responsible came to a head. His real trouble lay in the fact that there was hardly any Government policy of which he completely approved.

When younger men complain to me of their failure to receive higher appointments, and of being forced to bury their talents in some minor post which offers no challenge to their capabilities, I tell them of Rihaz: how he had been happy as a junior officer in a District and how he had loathed his senior assignment at Headquarters. To his last day he remained the champion of the Little Man, the worker from the village. But all he could do from the Secretariat seemed to be of small value, he contended, once adding in his abrupt way that in his position he was like a man belching against thunder.

Yet his village friends did not forget him; they knew he would love them, even after his retirement, as long as he lived. When at last he died, they set up a memorial to him in Venkatapur, and within a short time the custom of placing before it humble offerings of fruit and flowers became an established ritual. Perhaps, long after the passing away of the last of those who actually knew and loved him, his memorial will become just another little wayside shrine like those set up all over India to honour some forgotten saint or deity, where the poor and ignorant offer worship day in and day out.

This, then, is the story of a particular little corner of rural India as seen through the eyes of an administrative officer at a critical period of world history when India was in rapid transition, fast approaching independence or having newly achieved it The area, known as Telengana, formed much of the eastern part of the Hyderabad State (now merged in Andhra Pradesh), which was relatively backward compared with the adjoining east coast districts of Madras, where Communist influence had already penetrated. Agrarian problems here were made more acute as it was an area dominated largely by Deshmukhs (literally 'heads of the country'), landlords sometimes on a very large scale, who derived their landed position and prestige from their origin, far back in the Hindu period, as collectors of land revenue on behalf of the government of the day. Although they were no longer employed as such by the Government of the State, their earlier position of power had enabled them to amass lands, and they had thus become a wedge between the Government and the tiller of the soil. These conditions, not generally prevalent elsewhere in India, made the area peculiarly vulnerable to agrarian agitation.

As in the rest of the country, the Princely State was divided up into 'Districts' of several thousand square miles; the head of the District (as was Rihaz) was the Taluqdar, who had under him subordinate officers in charge of smaller units, down to the village officials. We shall hear much of these last. They were the Patel, the headman and collector of land revenue in the village, and the Patwari, the keeper of the elaborate records of cultivation and the land revenue accounts.

The full story of the Communist revolt in a region sunk deep in poverty and ignorance has not yet been written, but in certain chapters of this record which Rihaz has left some important aspects of that upheaval—and the events from which it sprang and the atrocities to which it led—are plainly set down, I believe, for the first time. The narrative set down may not be in consonance with chronology and may not follow the rigidities and restraint which a factual representation may demand, for it is a transcript of an impressionist mind in an environment charged with exotic ideals. But this does not affect the value of the narrative, because it records the typical reactions of various persons to the events of that time. These reactions belong essentially to the period when he penned those notes. Doubtless the reactions today would be different, and to set them down now in retrospect, in the light of all that took place in the years that followed, would be to assess rather than to record events. This, therefore, is not the history of a period; it is a contemporary narrative of some events and of the emotions they aroused during certain times of stress.

Such a narrative has its own place in India's national annals. All of us need to have some knowledge of the difficult times through which certain areas of India passed some years ago in order that we may be better prepared to understand the present and plan the future. The very fact that we can now objectively discuss those troubled times and strained relations is itself proof of how much has since happened and of the stability which India has since then achieved. This is a happy augury; for when we find ourselves willing to ponder over the events of the past, dispassionately and without prejudice, we give proof of a courage and a vision which will stand us in good stead in facing the future. Whatever else we may or may not do, we shall at least not repeat the mistakes which we have learnt to discover and identify.

ZAHIR AHMED.

Part One

THE OLD INDIA

I   Cleaning up a Village

'WE start tomorrow, and we'll start at Venkatapur, Mahboob', I said. (Mahboob was the newly appointed Assistant Collector). 'There is ample scope there for rural improvement. I have visited Venkatapur before; it is the filthiest, poorest and most disease-ridden village in the entire district. Yes, it is a pukka plague spot. If you can make something of Venkatapur, nothing else will ever daunt you!'

There was no road to Venkatapur, not even a cart-track; only a meagre foot-path which wound its way through fields and grass-less grazing land, past bushes, rocks and ravines. Even so, it was little used, for this isolated community of seven hundred-odd inhabitants found it difficult to go to neighbouring villages even in dry weather, while during the rainy season they found themselves almost completely cut off.

Leaving the main road, Mahboob and I rode for Venkatapur on ponies. A thick mud wall, browned by many suns and built centuries ago, surrouned the village. When several furlongs away we could see through the trees the remains of the crumbling walls. We picked our way cautiously through an algae-covered swamp, the smelliest spot I have ever traversed. As we moved across it, the smallest and largest forms of life in the region—the mosquito and the village buffalo—rose from their buzzing and their wallowing, as though to protest against our intrusion.

With an effort out of keeping with their size, our faithful ponies finally took us across this quagmire and we found ourselves on the narrow strip of a cleared path a few feet from the wall. We were forced to ride for half a furlong before we could locate an opening. The undergrowth soon became so thick that finally we had to abandon our ponies to the mosquitoes and continue on foot. We found an entrance at last—an impressive monument

3

to the designing ability of some Deshmukh (landlord) of an earlier century and, perhaps, to the skill of his masons who fashioned the wall; but inside we saw only one person, a small-statured lad of ten years, scrofulous, flea-bitten and emaciated. His attitude of resignation gave way to surprise and fear on seeing strangers within the wall. After a moment of staring at us, he led us silently into the enclosure and down a narrow lane past heaps of garbage and dung to the Chowdi, a low, thatch-roofed room, which served as village office-cum-rest-house. Here, weary, we plumped ourselves down on a sagging low cot held together by thin pieces of rope while, without any orders from us, the lad slid off to tell the village officials that we were there.

'Well, Mahboob?' I queried, with a faint smile.

He brushed away the flies, and shuddered. His planning, his education, his years at an Engineering College, had hardly prepared him for this reception. I watched him silently for several minutes. His eyes flitted nervously around the open room; he rubbed his hands, stroked his brow, finally rose and walked to the raised platform in front. After a few minutes of waiting for the local dignitaries, we decided to tour the village and, with an escort of yelping dogs, made our way down the narrow path. Even in the so-called main street, Mahboob's natty jodhpurs were generously splashed with mud and ordure. We walked on, past crowded huts whose doorways were jammed with women holding their tots and attempting to keep the other members of their broods in the enclosures, away from the visiting intruders.

Here and there, an old man sunning himself by the path would look up, favour us with faint recognition and then look away. A cow in the centre of the path held us up while she splashed dung in our way, then ambled aside. A goat brushed against us, then scampered off. Smoke was rising, steam-like, through the thatch of some of the roofs. At our heels had gathered many skinny children of all ages with blown-up bellies and running noses, in rags and dirt, who had slipped away from their guarding mothers to form a part of the parade. Cackling chickens, with elongated necks and frightened looks, ran about aimlessly. One chicken in its alarm took wing and flew in front of us right over the nearest hut.

In front of the huts were small scummy pools of putrid water, full of flies and mosquitoes which zoomed off as we approached and made their way, no doubt, into the sanctuary of the villagers' homes.

The weaver, then the potter, looked up as we trod alongside their huts. The other men then in the village (and they were but

4

few, for it was the time when all who could labour were needed in the fields) glanced up at us for a moment, then continued their somnolence. At last, after skirting several more cesspools breeding mosquitoes, we reached a slight rise at the end of the path.

'My God!' Mahboob cried in despair. 'Where on earth can one start? Everything seems to be', he continued slowly, 'first priority.'

To the left of us, in front of a mud hovel which appeared a little better situated than the rest, an old woman was fanning the embers of a small cooking fire. She brushed the air with a thin bunch of straw, looked placidly and shyly at me, drew part of her sari over her face as our eyes met, then resumed her work. I think it was there and then that I began to understand the basis of what she made of us. She measured us up, accepting us as those having authority, as men who realise the ages of social and economic duress through which her people had lived but probably did not much care about them. As far as she was concerned, she would permit us to stand there and ask her questions, even though she would keep her cold, searching eye on us, especially when problems of her own family's lands and taxes were brought up for discussion; it was obvious that she herself knew very little about those problems. She fanned away at the fire and Mahboob reared back on his heels and looked stolidly at her. I decided that I would break the spell of this tableau.

'Come, come', I said to him. 'Let us look inside some of the houses.'

'Talli', I said to her, using the local word for mother, 'may we enter your house?'

Laying aside her makeshift bellows, she rose stiffly, somewhat hesitatingly, but with a shy smile, and for a moment eyed us with a judicial aplomb worthy of the Supreme Court in Delhi! We must have passed muster for she acceded to my request: she would confer upon us the honour asked of her. She would permit us to enter the house and home which, though shabby, represented her sole centre of life and was truly sacred to her. Hesitating again for a few seconds she emitted a sigh of resignation, opened the sagging straw-made door, called to her husband that 'Durra' was entering, and allowed us to walk past into the one windowless room, while she walked out of the door. At the entrance, on the left, was hung a dried pumpkin, believed to bring prosperity. The hut was almost circular with a mud wall, roughly but thickly made, and a roof of sticks and palm leaves.

Through the door we saw, dimly, a few rags of bedding in one corner and, near them against the wall, three earthenware pots of varying sizes, balanced one over the other. We could also

5

see two other earthenware pots and a pumpkin slung by three bits of rope from an old bamboo, darkened by years, across the two walls. In a crudely carved niche in one of the walls was a punti, a mud saucer, with a burnt wick made of twisted rags. The floor was smeared with cow-dung, diluted with water, as a disinfectant. There were some floral designs drawn on the cow-dung to ward off evil. In another corner of the hut was a stone slab half sunk in the floor with a depression in the centre for grinding spices. There was nothing else in that hut.

In the far corner, like some gnome from another world, squatted an old man clad only in a scanty loin cloth, gulping gutka*. As I stepped forward, he put his hand over the dish to ward off the evil eye, for, according to superstition, outsiders should not see food being eaten. Then he stood up, and I guessed that he was offering us his hospitality.

'Thank you', I said, 'but we have already eaten. Sit down.'

He licked the last bits of porridge from his bony fingers, rushed out of the hut to wash his hands, came back, picked up a nondescript rag from the floor, dried his fingers and tied the rag over his head to show respect to his visitors. He then took up the conversation where it had been broken off.

'And I, sir, have eaten well today', he replied slowly. 'Yesterday I had no food, but today someone gave me work. I gathered a few annas, so I have eaten. Tomorrow, tomorrow', he mused, 'God only knows if I shall eat tomorrow. Maybe He will permit me to have buttermilk; sometimes I have much, sometimes none. I have only one buffalo and for the last week her milk has been dried up by an evil spell. And how can a poor man afford to sacrifice a goat to propitiate the spirits?'

He looked at us quizzically. I asked him if he owned any land. He said he was the qauldar (tenant) of the Bania, the village money-lender, who paid him all the expenses of cultivation, seeds, manures, etc, and supplied him with a pair of bullocks. At harvest time eighty per cent of the net grain had to be given to the Bania and twenty per cent was retained by him. That year, however, he said the crops had failed as there had been no rain.

'Have you any children?' I asked.

'Yes, two boys. One has gone in adoption to a nearby hamlet and the other works with the Patwari of another village.'

We had nothing to say. We turned, left him and his woman, walked back into the lane and on past the weaver's yard.

'And why do you think he came into our hut?' asked the old woman, with fear in her voice.

* Porridge. (For Indian terms not explained in footnotes, see Glossary, p. 143.)

'Oh, he just wanted to see how we live, perhaps. Don't fear, woman, he means no harm. He was just curious. Didn't you see he called you "Talli" and he knows our language. He seems to be a good man. This hut is as strange to him as his palace in the city would be to us. Did you see, he thought we were offering him food, as if we would dare such a thing. If he had even smelled this gutka he would have got a stomach-ache.'

We passed the temple, the only stone-roofed structure in the village, and went up to the school building, a dark room some twelve feet square, without windows, without furniture, without blackboard. We stood at the door. Here, squatting on a strip of battered leaf-matting were half-a-dozen pupils, all little boys whose swollen bellies and enlarged spleens told of malnutrition and chronic malaria. The schoolmaster, whose grubby dhoti (his loincloth) failed to hide some diseased skin patches, sat comfortably by the door, monopolising the light. The air was thick; apparently he had been smoking a bidi—a home-made cigarette. He was chewing betelnut. It was evident that visitors were neither expected nor welcome. The scene angered me and I was tempted to give vent to my feelings; however, I controlled myself.

'Come outside, Master Sahib', I said. 'Let the boys out for a spell before they all suffocate.'

Surprised, he stared at me, then motioned the boys out of the semi-dark prison. He rose and shuffled, blinking, into the sunlight. Immediately he felt himself challenged and began talking to us about his school. Twenty boys were on the roll but few attended regularly. The others had to look after the family cattle.

'And who pays you?' I asked. 'What is your salary?'

'Sir, I am paid from the "local funds". I receive ten rupees a month for my long hours with these lads.'

And ten rupees worth of ability and enthusiasm was about all the village got from this man. We talked a while. Some of the boys leaning against the dirty school-house wall looked on and waited, before I lost my temper with him. I turned away and we went on down the crooked path.

We went past the only big houses in the village, the property of the Patel and the Patwari and the Deshmukh, the money-lender and the landowner. On we moved, by the huts of the little people and through the dirtiest lane I have ever seen. It smelled pungently of urine and cow-dung and it sloped down to the village well, where some of the women were now drawing water for drinking and cooking, while others were washing their clothes nearby.

7

'Here is your first priority, Mahboob', I said.

A hundred yards away, covering an acre of waste land, was the Dhedwada, the area of the Untouchables. Nothing I have seen before or since exceeds in degradation the homes of these Harijans, the 'children of God' as Mahatma Gandhi called them. Here were not even houses of mud, but mere huddles of huts and shacks, made of sticks and palm leaves, standing barely five feet high and surrounded by heaps of garbage. With no windows and an earthen floor and a roof which kept out the light but did not repel the rain, they gave little protection and less comfort to the pathetic souls forced by a cruel social edict to live in that isolated part of the village. In front of these hovels there was not even a pretence of a street, but only a rough narrow path which had been worn through piles of dirt by the pressure of generations of bare feet. The only structure of a somewhat better standard was the open-air temple which these pitiful people had erected for themselves. In it they had placed an image of Maisamma, the Goddess of Smallpox.

Of course, there was no water well for these people, and they could not use the village well, polluted though it was. The Untouchables had to draw water from a distant pond outside the village. We looked around and moved on.

By evening our tents had arrived and we had them pitched in a mango grove to the north of the village. I sat in a camp-chair in front of the tent and watched the parade of gaunt men and women as they trudged from the nearby fields in the early twilight. The lean cattle were driven by emaciated children who would pen them for the night in the family living rooms. The pall of blue smoke now rising from the cow-dung fires hung in a low cloud over the huts. Intermingled with every activity of the villagers were the familiar noises: the lowing of cattle, the bleating of sheep, the barking of dogs, the chattering of women, the crying of children. I could even hear a more masculine note from the direction of the toddy shop. Suddenly night fell; only a few crude oil lamps flickered in feeble attempts to dispel the darkness.

After supper the people were drawn from their huts by beat of drum to the Chowdi—the village hall. I was to speak to them. I studied them as they came up and sat down. They seemed to breathe a spirit of apathy, and somehow to be proud of it. I knew they would not be easy to handle. I called them to order and tried to arouse them from the cloud of indifference which seemed to envelop them. I talked of their work, of the profits which would accrue to them if only they used the new methods of farming which I proposed to teach them; of how they should help them-

8

selves and not merely rely so complacently on a paternalistic Government. No comments followed my talk. The villagers merely went back to their huts. I then went to our tent and sat late into the night working out a detailed plan of operation for Mahboob to follow.

Cleaning teeth is a social ritual in the village. It is also the occasion for a review of events of the previous day. A neem twig provides both the toothbrush and the toothpaste, chlorophyll and all. The richer folk loll on their cots and clean their teeth; the humbler ones gather at the old well under the shady pipal tree.

Life here was always more placid, less serious, more sincere. These, too, were human beings, though they were treated as the dung heap of the community. They had no determination to go forward, perhaps, but they also had no cruelty in their minds; they were not intelligent, but they were not ruthless; they had no aspirations, but also no disillusionment; they never fought for a cause, but also they never destroyed for a cause. They were not leaders of humanity, they were plain human beings. But you could love them; you could not, however, always look with affection on the higher castes there in the village. How many different nations there were in this community! You could distinguish them from the way they smoked. The officers out in the tents smoked Wills' Gold Flake; the Patel an Indian brand, Charminar; while the neeradi,* Pochiah, who carried a wooden stick, flat at the end, which announced his official standing, and who had collected the crowd for my meeting, now relaxed and smoked a clay pipe of uncured tobacco with a piece of glowing coal on top of it. Then there was Tammari Baliga who enjoyed smoking his tobacco wrapped in a banyan leaf. Whenever the exigencies of social decorum demanded a pause in smoking, he merely stuffed the contraption in his turban and went about his work, reeking of tobacco and occasionally smoking from the head like a chimney. Here was Golla Sayiga, a true proletarian who in slack seasons worked on a gang which broke stones for the Public Works Department: now, in a period of relative prosperity, he puffed nonchalantly at a bidi. The school teacher was also here. He had been for so long in the village that he had come to be everybody's confidant. He took no more than an academic interest in their problems, but he was tremendously inquisitive all the same.

'Why did you bother to attend the meeting last night?' he asked.

'What do we know?' replied Baliga. 'This fellow Pochiah came round and told us that the Patel wanted us at the Chowdi

* An hereditary village servant who supervises the distribution of irrigation water.

9

and so we went. But Pantulu,* I couldn't follow what the Durra said in the Bhasha (language).'

But Golla Sayiga was smarter. 'Don't you know', he said with contempt for the stay-at-home, 'he was talking of how we could increase the yields. He asked us to use the white powder (fertiliser).'

'Yes! And destroy our crops, is it?' remarked Pochiah.

'How's that?' the teacher asked.

'Ayyo, Pantulu', he replied, 'this white powder drinks up more and more water and, as you know, if we do not get good rains up to Aslesha† the tanks will be only half full and after a few waterings the crops will dry up. It contains a lot of heat, and it burns up the crops if a lot of water is not given.'

'Yes', said Sayiga, 'it may be all right for the Patel's fields; they are all near the tank and they get water throughout.'

'Pantulu', asked Baliga, 'who was this Durra who lectured last night?'

The teacher explained he was the Talukdar Sahib, the Head of the District.

'Is he bigger than the Tehsildar Sahib‡?" Baliga asked.

'He's got all the Tehsildars under his thumb', replied Sayiga, with a touch of pride at his greater knowledge of the official hierarchy.

'Then can he get me some extra land, this Talukdar Durra?' asked Baliga, shuffling a little nearer to the teacher.

'Don't be foolish', interrupted Pochiah. 'That is the Girdawar's job§; why do you trouble this Talukdar Sahib for that?'

'No', objected the teacher, 'this Sahib is the right man; ask him. He will help you', he added.

'Don't give him wrong ideas, Pantulu', pleaded Pochiah. 'We are humble folk, we should not approach this big Sahib. The Girdawar Sahib comes every week; it is he who does the Panchanama.‖ If we pay the Patwari he will get it done through the Girdawar. We should not over-reach ourselves; we should keep to our proper places.'

'Nonsense', he said, irritated at Pochiah's cowardice and ignorance. 'He is the proper man. Ask him after the meeting tomorrow.'

---

* A term used for school teachers; sometimes for high-caste Brahmins.
† A certain period during the monsoon.
‡ Head of a part of a District called a 'Tehsil'.
§ A revenue inspector.
‖ A statement drawn up and attested by five persons following a kind of inquest after any offence or dispute.

The second meeting had been in session for some time. Better farming, improved yields, village drains and roads had been discussed. Everybody had listened with obedient but unintelligent attention and here was this trio blissfully smoking away and yawning. The teacher could not stand the apathy of Baliga. He was determined to bring this fellow to us. Perhaps he wanted to please me; perhaps, eventually, he even expected a reward from Baliga. Anyway, he dragged Baliga to our camp and put his question.

'Durra, what about land for us Madigars, especially for us, the Kavalkars?'*

'Is there any land?'

'Yes, Durra', replied Baliga. 'There is that low-lying land to the south of our village. We want that land; we have applied so many times, Durra, but still we have not got it. We are dying, we are slaves, we have nothing to eat.'

'How much land have you?' I asked.

'Nine "guntas" inam Durra, and all our people who are asking for this land have no more. We are your servants, Durra. We carry the Patwari's records to the Tehsil office; we help him in revenue collection, and when Sahibs like you come we are here to give our lives for you. We want a little land to live by, Durra.'

'What's this, Patwari, why has there been the delay? Are you up to any tricks again?' I demanded, touched and irritated.

The Patwari stood with folded hands in true Indian humility and servility. He let the storm pass, and then explained how he was trying to help but how there were difficulties. Part of the land was village grazing land; there were many complications.

'All that is nonsense, I want none of it. We shall go there tomorrow morning before I leave and settle the case.'

There was a glow in Baliga's eyes; he did not understand my words, but he could understand the tone and the intention. The Patwari whispered something to the Patel. When we were about to disperse the Patel came forward, half bent in respect, and slowly muttered: 'Durra, that land you wanted to see, shall I ask for horses in the morning?'

'How far is it?'

'It's on the village boundary, Durra, on the other side of the stream. It will take time.'

'All right, Girdawar Sahib, you go there tomorrow. I want a report by the day after; if not I will suspend you from service.'

* The Madigars are a caste of Untouchables; the Kavalkar is an hereditary village servant who acts as watchman.

11

I turned to Baliga and explained: 'Go with the Girdawar Sahib and show him the land; I shall see that it is done soon.'

'I shall look to your troubles. Do not worry. Come with me', said the Girdawar to Baliga in a most paternal fashion.

Baliga was stunned. He looked daggers at the teacher.

'What did I tell you?' said Pochiah. 'Why did you go here and there? You should have gone to the Girdawar Sahib through the Patwari.'

Crestfallen, Baliga and his friends turned back towards the village.

'What about the programme shown by the officer?' the teacher asked, more as an attempt to change the subject. 'Aren't you going to help yourselves by doing all he taught?'

'Where is the time, Pantulu?' asked Pochiah. 'We work on our lands; we work on the Patel's lands; we do yetti* for the Patel and the Patwari; we do yetti for Government officers. Where is the time for us to attend to these roads and drains? Our fore-fathers lived like this and we shall also have to live like this; we must work to get something to eat. How can we think of other things?'

'Further, what is the Government doing?' asked Sayiga. 'Why doesn't it do all this for us?'

'What!' the teacher shouted. 'And you want the Government to clean your drains and sweep your streets? This is your work; you must do it. You sweep the landlord's house. Why don't you sweep your own street?'

'We sweep the landlord's house because we get some grain. Who will pay us for sweeping our streets; and what is the Government doing? What is happening to all the land revenue we pay? The tank is breached, the Chowdi is collapsing; we are paid three rupees each month. What is happening to all the money? Why don't they do something about it?' Sayiga's logic was invincible.

'Government is maintaining your security. You and your property are safe because of Government. Otherwise what would have happened to you?' he answered meekly.

'What would have happened, Pantulu? What have we to lose? What have we that needs protection—our jobs? We our-selves make the posts; no one else would or could perform such duties. No, we have nothing to lose. The Government does nothing for us except take the land revenue.'

Sayiga was different from the rest. He was thinking, and

* Forced service, rendered without remuneration, extracted sometimes by landlords and officials.

such men are dangerous. Stone-breaking had made a different man of him. One wondered what role such Sayigas would play in future. For the present the teacher was beaten in the argument. He sheepishly slapped Sayiga on the back and went his way to the school. Some poor boy would pay with the skin of his back for this lost argument.

Some weeks later I returned to Venkatapur, this time accompanied by the District Local Fund Engineer and the Medical Officer. The physician was most welcome, for he carried dressings and huge quantities of quinine and magnesium sulphate—standard drugs by this time in the lives of these people. Long ago they had learned of the healing powers to be found in the doctor's little bottles.

Before doing anything else, I told the Patwari and the Girdawar that I was going to inspect the plot of land said to be partially grazing land and which was wanted by the Kavalkars and others. This created quite a stir. Everybody seemed to be whispering to the others; quick glances were being exchanged. With the help of the Measuring Inspector, whom I had also brought with me, we carried out a detailed inspection by nightfall and found that even after leaving the grazing land out of account, there was enough vacant Government land which could easily have been allotted to all who had been wanting it for years. But the Patwari's nephew had had an eye on it and enough of the Girdawar's interest could not perhaps be independently purchased by Baliga and others! I was able to pass orders for the preparation of maps, showing each person's allotment, and to make necessary entries in the village registers. This quick action had an electric effect on the attitudes of the people and on my future programme. What Baliga had to say to Sayiga and Pochiah on the subject that night I do not know, but the grant of small governmental loans the next week for the purchase of a pair of bullocks and an improved plough for each grantee created a sensation which spread into the adjoining villages.

Our visit was during the festivals of Holi and Moharrum.* It seems strange nowadays to recall how Hindus and Muslims, then so harmonious, joined so readily in one another's processions, entering one another's homes at the happy moment, and attacking one another with nothing more lethal than garlands of flowers and scent and coloured water. And as for the officers in charge, it never occurred to us to consider whether a village petitioner, let alone one of our colleagues, was a Hindu or a Muslim.

* Holi is a Hindu festival; Moharrum, a Muslim festival. Although a period of mourning in the villages, it does not remain so.

13

Even though I had not expected to find Mahboob pleased with what he had been able to do since my previous visit, I was disappointed to find him cross and despondent. Quickly he summarised his attempt to improve the villagers' conditions and their indifference to most of his proposals. He appeared crestfallen that he could not show his senior officer a better record.

'Come now,' I said, 'I didn't expect miracles of you. Tell me the worst.'

'They are a hopeless people, sir', he replied. 'They just don't want their conditions to improve. And the worst of it', he continued, now rather excited, 'is that the Deshmukh and the Bania, who are educated and who should have been the people's leaders, are the most obstinate of the lot; and I think the Patwari and the Patel are just egging them on. I no longer expect help, I have no hope of co-operation. Still', he added, speaking slowly, 'they might at least show some gratitude for what we are trying to do for them.'

I laughed. 'A few more years in the service, and you'll forget the word "gratitude".'

And then, even though I could have easily anticipated his answer, I asked, 'But what about those experiments in democracy you were going to carry out?'

'A complete flop, sir, and you probably guessed it! My Panchayat* would do nothing; my Debt Reconciliation Board wouldn't even work. They liked being on the committees, but that was all.'

'Never mind', I consoled him. 'I never thought you would have a hundred per cent success. But you have accomplished something, I know that. At least, I can see that you have made them clean up the village a bit. That is something. But tell me about the Deshmukh and the village worthies.'

'That badmash, that blackguard!' he snarled. 'The Deshmukh is nothing more than an idle, useless parasite. He does absolutely nothing but represent the land owners. The peasants, as you know, cultivate the land. Their crops are harvested under his supervision, and he takes almost all of the income, so he can continue to squat here and do nothing. Think of it! At harvest time the poor devil who has been in that field, he and all his family, for months and months, receives for his labours only a small dole of grain and three rupees a month, while his abominable boss puts the rest into his own pockets! And there starts the cycle, the terrible cycle of events through which these poor people have to go. The peasant can't live on his pittance, so he must go on

* A village Council of Elders which settles disputes.

14

borrowing. Then there will be a wedding or a funeral, and now and then a famine. Generations have been piling up these debts and these poor devils must slave away without the slightest hope of ridding themselves of the debts of their grandfathers and their great-grandfathers. Yes, at times I surely wish our people were not so honest and did not place so much emphasis on meeting these obligations which were incurred long before they were born.

'And the only chance the villager has', he continued, 'is also to go to Pulliah, the Bania, borrow more and more money, even though he must pay all the way from thirty-seven and a half to seventy per cent compound interest! I tell you, debts multiply like germs in a dung heap, and the whole system infects everyone in the village!'

'I know, I know', I said reassuringly. 'I know; it's the same everywhere. This situation isn't new to this village, nor is it new to India. But tell me', I added quickly, in the hope of getting him off his diatribe, 'have you checked the literacy of the people?'

'Only eight people in the entire village can read and write', he answered solemnly. 'They don't want to learn. They are not worried over that, or over malaria, even though we have ninety-eight cases on hand just now.'

'You said your Debt Reconciliation Board wouldn't work', I said. 'What is the situation there?'

'Well Pulliah, local Shylock that he is, has used every legal formality he can bring up to thwart me. He has even made these poor people give him receipts for twice the amounts he has actually advanced them. But how can we prove such a crime against him when the victims themselves will vouch that his figures are correct rather than take the chance of annoying him. The man is a medieval gangster, I tell you!'

'At least', I commented, 'you are learning lessons never taught you and the other lads in college. But now tell me what have you done with the Untouchables?'

'Of course, all the dirty work of the village falls to their lot', he replied. 'As elsewhere, they are the scavengers, the night-soil sweepers; they do all the forced labour, and for their effort they receive only the skins of dead animals and a small bit of grain when the harvest is good. I do not see how they live on such a little, but I must say I could not have done without them. Someone, you know, just has to do the dirty work.'

Next day I inspected the village records and, as a result, promptly suspended both the Patel and the Patwari. When the Deshmukh called, I refused to see him. But I did send for

Pulliah, the Bania. When he arrived I offered him no seat and kept him waiting for at least twenty minutes.

'You are obstructing debt-reconciliation work', I declared abruptly, when I was ready for him. 'If the whole affair is not settled properly within twenty-four hours, I fear there will be some trouble in this village. I shall consider this case in the morning. Be here at ten o'clock, sharp.'

He hastened to make excuses, but I refused to hear them.

The next morning that quartette of thugs, the Patel, the Patwari, the Deshmukh and the Bania were at my tent in good time. In the background stood the poor helpless ones who owed them money and who were ordered to be present.

Yelliah was leaning on his stick and watching the proceedings with apparent indifference, but with a glint of agitation in his eyes. He was a village servant and so had been his forefathers. They had received land for this service; after generations of sub-division at successions, Yelliah had a small bit of land still left to him. For the rest, he eked out a livelihood by working as an agricultural labourer, especially for the Patel. His close contact with the Patel and other official dignitaries had given him an inkling of the genuine and unchallengeable power of the Patel and Patwari. He knew better than to cross their path. He also knew that short-circuiting them got one nowhere. He knew too that you might give petitions to the Ruler himself, but ultimately they came back to the Patel for report and 'necessary action'! He was not angry at this; he accepted it. It did not strike him that there was any injustice in it. No, this was the order of nature and of the gods. After all, if you by-passed the goddess Maisamma, you got smallpox! If you by-passed the Patel, you got trouble from him. This was the law of causation; it was not social injustice. Justice to him meant repaying of debts. He owed a hundred rupees to the Patel; he would work for a year for the Patel. Such was justice. If the Patel did not return his silver bracelets after that, it would be injustice. But the Patel would never do such a thing. He was a man of honour. If the Patel, however, gave him only seventy rupees, saying that he would calculate a debt of one thousand rupees at the end of three months since the rest was interest, such action would not constitute injustice. That was the offer. Take it or leave it. After all, he was the only man who gave you the money so easily and without even a thumb-impression. And so Yelliah was intrigued at all this fuss. Why was this Sahib abusing the Patel? Government said they would start a Society. Very well, would the Government give

16

loans like the Patel on the spot without a khagaz (a paper or document)? But then all these Sahibs had some kink or other. This Sahib's kink was to start Societies. All very well, but the Patel alone has to run the Society. This Sahib tipped him for his services and did not ask for forced labour, so one could excuse him his fads. But if he wanted Yelliah to speak against the Patel he was mistaken. The Patel was a Durra. Yelliah was his tenant on some lands. Yelliah's father had been all these things to the Patel's father. If any high Government official wanted to bring Yelliah into trouble, he would be no party to it. What was the Government to him and he to the Government?

Baliga was smoking in front of his hut. He also wanted to be no party to this business. Sayiga had called him, but he would not go. Why did Sayiga want trouble with the Patel? No doubt the Patel was a cheat. He always calculated that you had to pay at least three times the correct amount. The Patel's father had been an honest man and a noble man; but this Patel was neither. He was glad that the Sahibs had come to give him a lesson. But the Patel had taken care of that. By getting those drains and cart tracks constructed by forced labour, he would please the Sahibs and the Sahibs would say no more. But these Sahibs were no fools; they meant business. Otherwise, why did one of them stay in this dirty village for so long? But Baliga would not go himself. Let Sayiga do it. After all Baliga had lands on lease from the Patel; if he lost them he would have nothing to eat; he was not a stone-breaker like Sayiga. These Sahibs came and they went, but the Patel was here always. He could drive Baliga out of the village. No, he would play safe. If and when the Patel was made powerless, he too would take his case and get it settled, but till then he would wait; after all, he had waited for so long, so long!

But some had come; some like Golla Sayiga. Golla Sayiga was squatting, waiting to be called up by the Sahib. He had no land anywhere. He worked seasonally as an agricultural labourer; he also worked in the gangs breaking stones. Such persons were always suspected by the authorities. Whenever a theft occurred the stone-breakers were the first caught and beaten. Of course, one of them would certainly have done it. But then, why should he be afraid? Nothing could be harder than breaking stones. Sayiga was here to speak against the Patel. Yes; he would tell the Sahib how he had been duped, how he had paid as interest three times the amount itself. Yes; he was not afraid of the Patel. But would the Sahib do anything? This Talukdar was a good man and appeared very different from others. Didn't he inspect the kharij khuta, the uncultivated Government land? There were rumours

17

that the Patel might be suspended. But the Patel might be too clever for the Sahib. Now the Sahib had started a Government Society, but who ran it? The Patel's cousin! They were all one; and the rules were such that people like him without land would get no loan. Who wanted loans other than the Deshmukhs? The more land you had the more loan you could get. All the same, Sayiga liked adventure, and here was adventure. He could speak against the Patel before the Sahibs. He had never thought of that.

Mahboob would read the record of each case while I cross-examined the creditor and the debtor. There were obstructions to our programme at first; the poor villagers were afraid to tell the truth about the transactions. The stern money-lenders were determined that these debts of generations should not slip through their fingers. When both sides finally realised that I would stay on the scene even for a month, if necessary, to settle these matters, they began to co-operate with me. When we had completed this labour, most of the debts were lessened by seventy per cent, fresh documents of indebtedness were drawn up and signed and the old ones destroyed.

As all the villagers were there, I used the occasion to tell them of other plans for their economic improvement in which they were asked to co-operate. Every landowner would pay into the village grain bank two seers of jawar for every acre he owned in excess of ten acres. Grain thus collected, I explained, would be lent out at sowing time to cultivators, who in turn would return it in kind at harvest time, plus ten per cent of the loan. The Deshmukh, who had stabled his cattle in a part of the old fort, would move his animals, so I stated, in order to make room for the school. Later, a new school building would be erected by the people, helped by Government. I myself would present the village school with a suitable blackboard and with new matting. Every cultivator, I told them, would dig compost pits, in which all dung and rubbish would be deposited. The owner of the toddy shop, I declared, on the authority of the Government which I had already obtained, had two months from that day in which to shift his place of business.

All of them, peasants and land owners, listened to my edict; they said nothing. They drifted away to discuss it all.

In spite of the fear of some of the people that we were wrecking the life pattern of their little community, changes were taking place, and slowly, all too slowly, the villagers first accepted them and eventually praised them. They had been dubious and even resentful, at first, about the physical changes which we had proposed, but after the cart-track was built, mainly through their own labour, connecting the village to the main road, they began to appreciate the work. They objected at first when we straightened and widened the village streets and built a drain from the well to a plot where they could grow vegetables. They raised no objection, however, when we dismantled the medieval wall that had encircled the village, or when, at the new site that had been chosen, we dug a well for the use of all the villagers irrespective of caste. They had adjusted themselves by this time to the changes; to changes that we hoped constituted progress.

To change the thought patterns and attitudes of the leading actors in this long drama, I started upon a programme of lengthy conversations with Pulliah, the Bania, and the land owners. It was for me to convince them that on the welfare of the village rested their own security. Most of them proved obstinate; they had been too long in the business. But at the back of their minds they realised that their twelfth-century economics could not last for ever. Some blindly resisted all change; to them their complex unchanging villages with their ancient temples and bad roads meant security. Only when they realised I was determined to alter these things did they go slowly and reluctantly along with me. I was, however, certain in my own mind that I could eventually bring about a transformation in their thoughts.

It was with Pulliah that my talks were most free and most frank. I was convinced that I could convert him to the importance of community uplift. I wanted him to see, further, that improvement of the peasant's condition would not mean his ruin.

I talked to him at length about our new Co-operative Credit Society and asked if the organisation would hurt his business. He did not think so; the Society took too long to do business, he said; it used too much red tape to suit the villagers. Often the villager wanted a loan to meet an emergency: for illness, for death, for marriage, for crop failure; he could not wait until the Society had given all the necessary approvals ere the loan could be made. It was no good a man's applying for a loan if it was eventually made to his children or his children's children, 'Less twenty per cent deducted', he added with a twinkle in his eye. And then he said, 'When I advance and collect money I know all the facts about the man, all the details of his business affairs —I make allowances for everything. A Co-operative Society cannot consider these personal matters.'

After I had penetrated his reserve and had won a certain measure of his respect he, who had at first insisted he was such a poor man, even confided to me where his money was hoarded.

19

'My father had a large well dug', he explained, 'and he filled it with silver rupees and a large quantity of sand; I use it today. So large, indeed, is the quantity of sand that if ten thieves worked for an entire night trying to empty the well, they would hardly find ten rupees for all their trouble.'

An ingeniously devised strong-room, I thought.

On another occasion, I questioned him about his initial opposition to our work.

'We did not understand at first, Sarkar', said Pulliah. 'When you and Mahboob Sahib came, we thought you would be like the other officials.'

'What sort of other officials?'

'Sarkar, I am a poor man. What do I know of officials and such great ones?'

'Pulliah, you are a very influential man and you certainly know about the officials in your own locality. How honest are they?'

Pulliah said, 'Sarkar, you cannot buy honesty for twenty-five rupees a month. The petty officials cannot live on this pay. Out of it they must pay a pittance to people at the Tehsil Head-quarters: the Peshkar*, the Jamabandi clerk† and the peon who serves official notices. Since these wages were settled, prices have gone up. Besides, formerly the village was self-contained, each family lived on the produce of its own land—lived simply, it is true, but *lived*. Now we raise cash-crops. We are dependent on the outside world, and if prices slump, we starve.'

'I never heard of money-lenders starving in a slump, Pulliah!'

'Sarkar, everyone attributes all his troubles to the money-lender because he must find someone to blame. But I am a poor man, I must live like anyone else. Aie! How can I live when you have cut down my lendings by seventy per cent?'

'You will have fewer bad debts, Pulliah.'

'I hope so, Sarkar, I do hope so. Eh! But we'll never be free from troubles. At least nowadays the magistrates and high officials do not take bribes much. You know old Qudrat Hussain Sahib of Fattehpur?'

'A splendid old gentleman!'

'He was a magistrate in this District once. It was the custom for the party to a suit to visit him about a week before the day of hearing and present him with as much as five hundred rupees in notes, if the case was an important one.

'"Villain!" Qudrat Hussain would say. "You dare to bribe

* A revenue official, Superintendent of the Tehsil Office.
† A clerk dealing with revenue accounts at the Tehsil Headquarters.

me? Cast the notes into the furnace!" and the money was then deposited in a stove in a corner of the room.

'A few days later, the opposite party would come and his present too was deposited in the stove. But the fire in that stove, Sarkar, was never, never lit! And Qudrat Hussain Sahib always boasted that he was never influenced by bribes, which was true enough for he kept the money of both parties and judged the case only on the evidence Of course, he returned the deposit of the losing party.'

On another occasion the school teacher was with me on one of my usual evening walks. I was telling him about the important role that a school teacher could play. He was pleading his own insignificance.

'Officers come and officers go, but they cannot replace local leaders', I said. 'If work is to be of permanent value it should come from the people themselves and with the best possible use of the local resources.'

'Villagers are like children, sir, and they need somebody like you to guide them', he replied.

'That's all right, but these children should be guided and inspired by their own leaders. If any programme is to survive it should be the result of people's own changed thinking and not what somebody tells them to do.'

This appeared to leave him unconvinced. I added after a pause: 'I want a powerful local Committee, elected by the villagers, to take up the work.'

'Who will be on the Committee?' was the prompt question. Finding me thinking, he said, 'If the Patwari, the Deshmukh and the Bania are on "the Committee", such a Committee will do more harm than good; and if they are not on it, the Committee will be powerless.'

A battle between democracy and tradition raged in my mind and tradition seemed to win for the time being. Yet I had my own ideas: the Panchayat and the Co-operative Society must be made really effective to break the entrenched pillars of authority and the economic stranglehold. But this was an end that could not be brought about by edicts and orders. It was a time-taking process and needed care and effort. Mahboob and I might not be here in this District long enough to see the fulfilment of the idea. Our successors might continue the effort, I hoped. But this belittling breed of 'successors' somehow always hunted for personal credit and many a promising scheme had been killed either for lack of understanding or in trying to see that the credit for the scheme was not even shared with the officer who was the originator.

2 Difficulties and Triumphs

ONE day, soon after we had arranged for the first spinning wheel to be delivered in the village, Mahboob came rushing into my office. I had anticipated some of his problems but for some strange reason I had not reckoned that he would have difficulty with that most ancient of troublemakers: religion.

Our people, in towns and villages, had developed a tolerance for the differing opinions of one another and Muslim, Hindu, Parsi and Christian had learned to live quietly with one another. True, there were fanatics of all faiths; evangelicals who first experienced the surge of love for the Higher Being and then felt themselves impelled to battle on behalf of the validity of their own belief, even though the religious freedom of others might be denied and the entire village or town be thrown into turmoil because of their evangelism. Crusades, battles and inquisitions in the name of religion were not unknown, even though in recent years they had, in that form, become the exception. I was distressed that this oldest of quarrels had appeared to thwart Mahboob.

'It broke out this morning', he said quickly as he stood in my office and rocked back and forth on the heels of his riding boots. 'It was all caused by our road survey. You see, sir, there's hell to pay with the road. Well we want to shift the alignment, but they won't stand for that a bit, even though I've already constructed a new building for housing the Alums.* It's tough, I tell you sir, it's tough!'

'Come now', I said as I motioned him to a chair to get him seated and relaxed. 'Surely they've just been pulling your leg a

---

* Banners with metallic or wooden symbols representing deceased Muslim saints.

bit. Like all human beings when confronted with something new in life, they feel your presence a challenge, a criticism of their way of life. They're not rebelling against you personally, Mahboob. They're just fighting it because it's something new. And besides', I added, 'they haven't much of a leg to stand on, you know; an Ashoorkhana* isn't a place of worship and I'm sure they know it, and we cannot have a straight road unless this dilapidated room is shifted.'

'I know that, sir', he replied. 'I thought about that, and even got a Fatwa from the Imam Sahib† to back me up when I talked it over with them, but right away Mohammad Ghouse started working among the dozen or so Muslim families to oppose it. And he's calling it religious persecution! As though I would persecute fellow Muslims!

'And then, to make matters worse', he rattled on before I could interrupt, 'the Hindus have taken the cue and are following suit; they are all stirred up because we want to move Hanuman, the Monkey God, so we can straighten the road running down to the huts of the Dheds—the Untouchables, you know. They won't take orders from me any longer.'

'You should have been firm with them in these matters from the very beginning', I declared sharply.

'They act as though I was robbing them instead of trying to teach them to live like human beings! These two religious fights make me sick! I tell you, sir, they make me sick!'

I realised that quick action had to be taken. The young man was deeply moved by the holding up of his plans for improvement and by the continual frustrations which seemed to block his every move.

'Leave these fights over religion to me', I told him. 'Do nothing about these issues. I shall see these people myself soon.'

'But I don't think . . .'

'I think you think too much at times. Sometimes in wrong channels. But remember, now I, not you, handle problems of religion!'

Next day I went to Venkatapur. After selecting a site for the new well to be dug, I walked with Mahboob to his tiny office, then asked him to send for Mohammed Ghouse.

'I'm not sure that is advisable', he countered. 'I should . . .'

'You should send for Mohammed Ghouse', I replied tartly, and sat back with hands folded until the trouble maker arrived.

---

* A building where the Alums are kept.

† Fatwa, a religious direction or verdict given by a competent authority; Imam, a religious leader.

23

'Mohammed Ghouse,' I said briskly, 'you may be able to play the fool with Mahboob Hussain Sahib; he is a young man just out of college; this is his first job. You shall not play the fool with me.'

'Sarkar', he replied feebly, shuffling his bare toes in the floor dust, 'I do not know what you mean.'

'Mohammed Ghouse, very very unpleasant things happen to people who stand in my way!'

The poor fellow stared at me for a few seconds, then nodded in assent. At last, having regained his composure, he said again, 'But Sarkar, I do not understand what you mean.'

'You shall understand. I mean the Ashoorkhana, Mohammed Ghouse, and you know it!'

Rubbing his hands, cringing slightly, he repeated, 'But I do not understand what you mean. I have not done anything.'

I have never been proud of myself for the rating I gave the poor fellow as he stood there in front of me. I knew that he alone was not responsible for the immediate difficulty; I was aware that many co-religionists and even others had objected to this change in the age-old location of the Ashoorkhana, and that many of them probably had urged my victim to stand his ground against Mahboob, the youthful intruder. Principles of belief, no doubt, were involved. And while I would not condemn any man for the manner in which he approached his God, I knew, as I continued to tongue-lash away at this pitiful man in front of me, that he represented the ultra-conservative. If we were to improve the conditions of our people quickly we must not be thwarted by ancient superstitions which halted our plans for progress. All morality, I argued to myself, was a form of coercion and, whatever the felt needs of the people, there were also their socially desirable needs in furtherance of which I should use my influence: persuasive influence, perhaps! Our people needed guidance, I said to myself, if they were to wake from their long sleep and slow decay.

'Not another word, Mohammed Ghouse!' I stormed. 'Move the Alums from the Ashoorkhana and do it *now*! Get a move on!' And while the poor fellow backed out of our presence and ran off, I turned to the equally surprised Mahboob and informed him that he could begin to dismantle the old Ashoorkhana within the hour and shift the Alums to the newly-built Ashoorkhana which Mahboob had completed last week.

My frontal attack on Mohammed Ghouse paid off better than I had hoped. He did as he had been told and the Alums were soon moved. I knew, of course, that gossip and comment about

24

my declaration would travel quickly through the little group of people. I wondered how the Hindus would react. I soon found out; they wanted to help. The speedy reaction to our move showed me not only their desire to help us solve this petty road problem, but also their willingness to co-operate in the big programme we were planning on their behalf. Their gift of land near the Hanuman temple, announced to me late that afternoon after we had tramped for several hours up and down those dusty village paths, was pleasant news. As a result of our efforts, the road was built as our engineers had aligned it, the people were given access from the village to the main road and these same men—Muslims and Hindus—continued their worship.

To me it was and continued to be significant that, in this single incident, we had given thought to the improvement of man's needs. We had not been slothful in our thinking, had not desecrated places of worship, nor slighted the beliefs of people. However, we had effected a major improvement in their physical well-being. Surely no deity would or should be offended by such labours.

Early next morning we were discussing our work for the day. Casually, somewhat naïvely, Mahboob told me of a recent incident and asked me how we would fight certain superstitions in the village. It seemed that Pulliah's grandson had been bitten by a cobra. The eight-year old had been given the traditional treatment outside the realm of medicine—cautery with red-hot iron—and, strangely enough, had survived. The difficulty, however, was with Pulliah; he had refused to permit the cobra to be killed; it represented the incarnation of some god and therefore must live! Mahboob looked depressed.

'By God, sir, there are times when I would like to call on Allah to curse all disbelievers!'

'Tut, tut', I remonstrated, trying not to show my amusement with his boyish dignity, and went on with my work.

'What are the people doing about making windows in their houses and about keeping their cattle out of the living room?' I asked.

'All right, as long as I am there to watch them', Mahboob replied. 'Then, as soon as my back is turned, they block up the windows. They drive the cattle right in by the front door. They're hopeless, absolutely hopeless, I tell you, sir! The only thriving business in the village is the toddy shop. The work we are doing on the roads has meant employment for these people; this has put a little money into their pockets, and about every anna of

25

it has been spent on drink. The liquor trade is enjoying a boom.'

'Not for long, I'm determined to stop it.'

'We won't be popular if we do that', he answered with a sigh.

'Neither was Socrates nor Jesus', I answered.

'I am hardly prepared to pay with my life for success on this job', was his reply.

I moved a finger down my check list. 'What about the grain bank?'

'Working fairly well', Mahboob answered as he sat down on a chair. 'I inaugurated it on an inauspicious day, so it seems; they had another event planned for then, and only a few of them paid me the compliment of being present. However, I have built up enough reserve to provide a small dole to the elderly folk. I administer it myself; I have found no one here I care to trust with funds or grain.'

'And the school?'

'I can report progress there. We have shifted it from that hovel, where you saw it working, to the old fort. The new teacher you sent us is young; he loves children, he is interested in teaching and I truly think he has the making of a good teacher.'

I nodded. This news was most pleasant to hear. 'The next step, I believe, should be the establishment of a Co-operative Credit Society for these people', I commented.

'Pardon me, but don't you think, sir, that this would be rushing them along too fast? You know what the villagers think about anyone who handles money. They will think that the fellow in charge is some new kind of tax collector and that'll put more trouble in my hands. And really I have enough as it is.'

'Cheer up, Mahboob', I answered, as I patted him on the back. 'There's no need for despondency. You're not doing so badly. Besides your success with the school and the grain bank, I noticed that some compost pits have been dug and that the entire place is noticeably cleaner.'

'Yes', he replied quickly, 'but not so much because of me. Some of those things were started by you, and others just "happened"; I don't feel, however, that much of the success was due to my so-called experiments in democracy. I had to jettison all that nonsense and even scrap my previous committees. I'm ashamed to say it, but I had to deal with them as though I were a dictator. Oh, I know it's all wrong, but by God there seems to be no other way to deal with these people! At times I think they listen to my orders only so that they can go away and do just the opposite of what I had directed!'

26

'It is only by patience you can win them. You must remember one thing', I said. 'We have to change their thinking and that is a slow process. You should win their confidence. Work done through fear does not last long.'

Then we talked of some funds which I would send down for the general village development, of the procedure to be adopted in closing the toddy shop, of the best way to use the spinning wheel in idle hours.

'There are other things for you to do, of course', I added. 'For example, try to get these people into the habit of spreading cow-dung on their fields and to stop burning it; there is plenty of brushwood around here to use. Then try to build up interest in such handicrafts as pottery, basket-making and wood-work.'

'But I don't know any handicrafts', remonstrated Mahboob.

'Good heavens! I never knew any either, until I started working with these people. Read up on the subjects, then get to work. But don't expect immediate results; it may be years before you can see any good coming from your labours. It calls for sustained effort. I see that you love these people, or you wouldn't be here, and that quality is most important in this work. Remember: you can win their confidence by patience, justice and fair play. Do not worry; you will do just that.'

A month later, when I returned to Venkatapur, I was met by a more satisfied Mahboob. He had closed the toddy shop, there were fewer living rooms housing cattle, the entire village was a cleaner place to live in. With me on this excursion was our physician, readily welcomed, as usual, for his supply of quinine and medicine for skin diseases. Also in our party were three Congress leaders. They were deeply impressed by seeing the villagers repairing their houses and, surprisingly enough, also making windows in the mud walls.

A short distance up the lane was one house which had given way during the rains. Its owner, an elderly woman standing nearby, told us that she could not afford to have it repaired.

'And furthermore', she added, 'the priest says it is not an auspicious time for such work.'

However, I had other ideas on the subject. Quickly I collected Mahboob and my visitor-friends and, after short consultation and preparations, we began to rebuild the mud hut. Several others joined us and within four hours the hut once more was fit for use.

In the quarter of the Untouchables, the Dhedwada, where we walked a short time later, we found heaps of rubbish still lying in our path. Mahboob looked apologetic. I took off my coat

27

and demanded a broom. Against the protests of my friends I began to sweep the street. Within a few minutes Mahboob, one of the visitors and all the Dheds had joined me in the work. The other high caste men who had come with me on this excursion slipped unobtrusively out of sight. They refused to clean up the debris of the Untouchables: the very shadow of the Untouchable would make higher castes unclean.

That evening, after the doctor had administered quinine to many villagers and had even been able to vaccinate some of them against smallpox, Mahboob, my Congress visitors and I sat in the faint twilight and talked of Venkatapur, of what it had looked like when I had first brought Mahboob there and of the state of things before our eyes. The conclusions were evident; homes were cleaner, health was better and the people were earning more than they ever did. Above all, we had helped to create some honest local leadership which was not there before.

I have thought of that evening many times; it seemed to be the first moment that we had been able to catch a glimpse of the progress which was being made.

Three years later, when I left the District, I was able to make another evaluation. Our initial changes had moved on and had bred other changes in the day-to-day life of the little community. It was in no way the same place it had been when Mahboob and I arrived. The residents were the same people, but their very appearance, their approach to life, their whole existence, had been altered so appreciably as to make them hardly recognisable as the same people who had passively suffered or merely existed in Venkatapur three years earlier.

Where there had been no connection with the outside world, there was now a road leading to the main highway; in place of dirt-cluttered lanes which wound about their huts, they had straight, clean streets; where that stagnant swamp had lain, to the south of their dwellings, was now a playground where the boys played football and the girls kolatam.* Now the school was flourishing; iron ploughs and better seeds made for better farm yield. There were latrines and compost pits, and windows had been installed in most of the houses, whose owners had been educated to the wisdom of keeping them open. Mahboob had worked well.

Venkatapur was still not a paradise and the people who lived there were not angels. After three years, in many ways they were still just the poor residents of an Indian village. Some were decent folk, some rogues. There was some cleanliness and awareness of

* A kind of folk dance.

the importance of modern health methods; but there was still dirt, still the ancient objection to any therapy which stemmed from a source other than traditional magic. However, after the three-year period, the people were living not as beasts but as human beings, and when they recalled in later days the changes that had taken place in their village life they admitted, sometimes reluctantly perhaps, that in some fashion Government had actually been responsible for more good than harm. And when I left the District, they accorded me the most precious form of homage : the homage of tears.

3 Communism Appears

UNLIKE most young officers in our Service in a similar situation, I fancy, I was depressed, not elated, at being transferred from the District to the State Headquarters. However, I had to go. In my new position I faced more difficult problems, but the real trouble was that my duties were much more impersonal than those I had rather enjoyed in the field. What I had to do on each piece of work was just exactly what I had to do in all preceding cases. Everything was the same, the same, the same. Worse still, my duties lacked the leaven of personal contact with village people. I could not find here the solace of creative work.

What really surprised me was that I encountered at headquarters many of the same enemies of progress I had faced in the villages. All of them were here: jealousy, corruption, backbiting, intrigue, nepotism, inefficiency; but they operated much more subtly than in the villages. At times people would display a brazen indifference to human problems in the background of their files. This is sometimes said to be part of the price we pay for civilisation.

I loved those people back in the villages, not only the friendly ones but all those others who had opposed me consistently when I had tried to improve their way of life. I liked to think that, in a few cases at least, the feeling was mutual. I felt that however far away I might be from them, I should never lose sight of their basic problems. How little I knew! For a while I did manage to retain contact with my friends in the District. There were letters, there were visits to my office, there were journeys to Venkatapur. Then I became even busier with files, files and more files. It was the old old story of administrative paper work, known all over the world. It came like the surge of the tide and, whether I cared for it or not, each case had to be noted and decided upon; and in each case, whatever its merits, one had to share the blame. After a while, some of my petty labours were shifted to others and I was given greater responsibility. Then, however, I found myself even further removed from the villages. Finally, after months of hard work at the new post, I suddenly discovered that my ties with my old stamping-ground had snapped. No longer could I maintain contact with those people. And while I sat in my protected and comfortable office room, the planet's very existence became involved in a frantic and urgent change.

World War II seemed to be quite remote from my office and its dull routine; it was even more distant from the people back in the District, living in their mud huts, on scrub-covered hills and in stony vales. The people in those villages were not a race who enlisted in the army. They regarded war, when they noticed it at all, with as little concern as they would have given to an earthquake or a famine striking some other planet. Yet the war hastened changes in the lives of those very people, and none, the lowly or the mighty, could halt the shift in the patterns of living which that world catastrophe brought in. Even though the authorities, especially the higher authorities, clung to the past with all the obstinacy of the cow that refuses to take notice of an onrushing train, developments did take place and left their mark on the lives of those little people. It was of course a time of great political upheaval throughout the world, but even shifts in power, in leadership, in forms of government, however rapidly they moved, were outpaced by the bewildering rush of economic change.

People in other parts of the world have had difficulty in understanding why a people as close to the soil as are the majority of Indians should be threatened by hunger in times like those. The fact is that Indian villages, largely self-contained as they are, nevertheless find themselves dependent on the world outside for many needs. This dependence, of course, is further accentuated in times of stress, when money will buy less and some articles, no matter how little of them may be wanted, are not to be had at all. The villager probably benefited socially from the after-effects of the war, but economically and spiritually he suffered.

First, food became dearer and, with the passing of the months, more difficult to obtain. Armies must be fed. Close to the soil as were the peasants, they could get but little from their marginal lands. Government stores, even though they were only a few miles away, were empty. Despite official attempts to solve the immediate problems of food by compulsory levies of grain and by the occasional confiscation of hoarded stocks of food, the difficulty swelled quickly into a crisis. Agitators exploited every situation to spread distrust, cynicism and hatred among all the people of the community as though they were spreading manure to speed the growth of their particular political theories. And as though these dispensers of subversive thoughts and political theories were not harmful enough to the peace of mind of the people, aggressive communal fanatics, in the name of their own faiths and security, must now enter the ring to stir up long-dormant passions, to incite hatred of Muslim for Hindu and Hindu for Muslim, relentlessly to project fantastic plans for impracticable and unreal theocratic states utterly remote from life in our modern world. Their advocates attempted to manipulate economic laws to their own liking. Why were not rupees and annas to be had for the family's work? Why was not food forthcoming, when people were willing to work for it?

A hungry man ceases to reason, we are told; and if this adage be true, there were many non-reasoning human beings within our community at the time. Unrealistic attempts to grab political power were being made by people who had not the faintest idea of administrative techniques; people to whom means were of no consequence. As people lost the habit of reasoning, it was not a long step first to the dread of fear and then to the fatal region of wild panic.

Throughout our part of the country there had been built up a peculiar condition, like mental illness. Little fears had grown into great troubles, which had blossomed into gigantic hatreds. The whole region seemed to be going to pieces. At that time I did not know what was happening; now I can see that, except for the post-war troubles, all these difficulties were most carefully planned and most ably brought about by fanatics who did not hesitate to burn men alive in the name of political freedom or in the name of their own security and to retain their own privileged position; and by agitators who promised paradise on earth if only some blood was shed and general confusion created. The pattern employed by these sinister master craftsmen (for such must I call them even though I think little or nothing of the results of their labours) is as old as the tenets of their creed. Intimidation, highway robbery, violence, murder, theft and arson were tools used to create first a sense of distrust, next, fear, and finally, panic.

As these incidents increased in number and mounted in severity, the Communists hailed them as lights on the highway leading to the great Class Struggle. Other agitators referred to them as separate battles in the fight for freedom. Communal fanatics thought that this was the opportunity to gain dominance and power. The administration made too little of them; it went placidly and unrealistically about its business of quelling disorder by means of sporadic and indiscriminate police raids and short prison sentences, like a man trying to extinguish a fire enveloping his house by pouring a cup of tea over the flames.

At Headquarters I had learned how slack and even corrupt government may prove itself to be at times. But as people became more panic-stricken and the whole fabric of law and administration appeared to be falling apart at the seams, I saw ever more horrifying examples of inefficiency and nepotism. The state, the single social organism which a citizen had a right to approach for help in times of trouble, now seemed to have run away from him. Of course this situation, far more vicious than ever the agitators themselves could have hoped for, was given wide publicity in every village. Reacting to this news, as though they had been deserted by their only friends, people became even more fretful and unrest eventually grew into rebellion. I was offered a senior appointment at that time to crush the Communist rebels, but I declined the post; I was convinced that the problem was far more serious than the policy makers realised and that the difficulties at hand demanded a solution far more drastic than the Government of the day was prepared to provide. It was a mistake, I thought, to fight such agitation with guns and prison sentences. We had to redress the glaring social wrongs and fight ideas with ideas. But it was clear that the Government clung to mediaeval policies and notions of administration. It was obvious that the torrent of human urges was struggling to burst the dams of feudalism.

Often, however, I attended meetings of officials charged with the responsibility of restoring order in the troubled areas. At one of these sessions I learned that several hundred rebels had been imprisoned in a cinema hall, for want of jail accommodation; they had been charged with offences of which, as it seemed to me, none of them could have been guilty. The situation perturbed me. After a day spent in worry about it, I asked for permission to talk to the prisoners. The local Inspector of Police was doubtful of the wisdom of my interviewing the 'dangerous' prisoners, but eventually I obtained permission from the Minister in charge of the police, an Englishman at that time, to see the prisoners.

In the large hall, poorly lighted by only two hurricane lanterns, I was confronted by hundreds of peasants. Most of them

33

D

were squatting on the floor. A few who were better dressed sat on benches. Terrified though they seemed to be, they hardly gave the appearance of rebels. I moved among them and, even though I was frigidly received at first, I managed to converse with this one and that one until finally I broke through their reserve. Then they talked to me.

And how they talked! They were not rebels. They were hungry frightened men who had been made victims of the widespread, panic-inspired tyranny of local police officers. The most serious of the crimes with which they could legitimately be charged was that of contributing small sums, under threat of death, to the party funds of the Communists and thereby technically becoming members of the party.

I made the facts known and very soon, after interrogation, the Minister ordered the release of these people. The following week the local Communist news-sheet gave him the recognition he might have anticipated. The publication read: 'At last Comrade Stalin has sent one of his own officers to secure the release of the prisoners at Sarampet. Despite the opposition of the Fascist Police, the Russian Officer fearlessly opened the gates of the concentration camp. Glory to Comrade Stalin! ... We have sent Comrade Anna Reddi to Moscow for machine guns and ammunition, and now we call upon all patriots and democrats to subscribe liberally to the fighting fund for their freedom. Those who hesitate or who withhold their wealth are traitors, hirelings of the Fascist war-mongers. ...'

Months later, in performing my duties in another post of Government, I visited the jails, by this time heavily packed with prisoners accused of participation in the 'rebellion'. Furtive and bewildered, they had more the appearance of stunned animals than of thinking men. One of those perturbed creatures I had known only a short time before as a prosperous farmer. Even though we had differed in our outlook, I think he was as happy to see me as I was to meet him, and I talked with him about the peculiar chain of events which had transferred him from his rice fields to this dirty cell.

'But why are you here?' I asked after our words of greeting. 'You should not be in jail, but out working on your farm', I added.

'I have turned against the Government', he replied flatly.

'But why?'

'Because you choose to rule us with the dregs of your bureaucracy, the scourings of officialdom', he spouted quickly.

The accusing polysyllables echoed sentiments akin to the

ones I had heard mouthed by some ambitious agitators in the District just after I had been transferred to Headquarters. In a mild way I attempted to defend the Government.

'You know we poor people cannot obtain justice from these menial people in Government', he replied, then walked away.

I asked an elderly man nearby why he had joined the rebels. Quickly he replied: 'Durra, these beasts said they would give all the land to the peasants, that there would be plenty of food at all times, that we would have no taxes. No Zamindar, no Deshmukh, no Patwari. And it is the Government and the police that have kept us out of this paradise!'

A few feet away were about twenty middle-aged men whom I recognised as farmers I had known in a village a few miles from Venkatapur. And they, like the old man who had left me for better company a few minutes before, appeared quite happy over the prospect of greeting one they had known. We chatted for a moment.

'But tell me', I asked bluntly, 'why are you people here?'

'Durra', replied their leader, whom I remembered well, 'we should not be kept here. We all are peaceful, law-abiding folk, who never troubled the Government or the police. You know our village. One dark night, about three months ago, all of us were awakened by gunfire and we rushed out of our houses to see what was the matter. The lanes of our village were as bright as day, for the Bania's house was blazing high.

'And what did we see by the light of the fire? Durra, we saw half a dozen men wearing masks over their faces, and carrying guns. There we saw the Bania, the Patwari and the Patel all tied to wooden posts. The masked men were flogging them, and the three who were tied were crying "Chachani-Banchoni", "Aya! I'm dead", "I'm your slave, Sir."

'Then, Durra, the raiders turned to us. They demanded our help. They had guns. We had no guns for we were quiet, law-abiding folk. Durra, what could we do? They demanded donations from us for the Communist Party. Durra, what could we do but give them money? If we had refused they would have beaten us, and they might also have beaten our families and burnt our houses. We gave them money. One of them made a speech about how we were being exploited and the freedom that was coming. Another hoisted a red flag on the village pole, then made all of us salute it. Durra, what else could we do?

'Then they ordered us to follow them to another village and we did. We saw them beat the Patwari and the Bania even there. Durra, perhaps some of us did some looting, but what if we did, and what else could we do? These men had taken everything from us, so we just took a little from our neighbours. And all the time, Durra, there were the men with the masks and the guns, watching to see that we did not run back home.

'Suddenly, as we stood there, shots were fired, and people whistled and shouted; the police swooped down and arrested us all. The men with the guns and the masks ran off to the jungle, to hide-outs selected in advance; but how could we, law-abiding men with homes and families, run away, and where could we go? Now, Durra, it is we who are locked here in jail; the men with the guns are still at liberty.'

Many were in prison, I found, just because they had run away from their homes to safety elsewhere and had not been able to explain satisfactorily to the police their presence in villages other than their own. Some were there because of the shameful use by the agitators of that most potent of devices, rumour. The tactics, old as our soil itself, have been well developed in recent years.

Someone would start the rumour that police officers were hunting for a particular resident of the community, and the 'grape vine' would perform its most effective work. The terrified people would swear allegiance and contribute funds. These same agitators would spread the word throughout the village that all the huts in a sister community would be raided within a short time. Then the people who lived in the village so designated would leave everything behind and flee to the jungle in panic. The gangsters would move in promptly, steal what they liked and move on to other more fruitful territory. Scores of people would flee, fearing the police scarcely less than the Communists. Others would be arrested as vagrants, people who had fled from the Communists who suspected them of helping the police.

I wished to learn from these men if there was any political pattern in this turmoil of raid and counter-raid, of arrest and flight, so I asked a number of these so-called 'Communist Rebels' what they understood by the term 'Socialism'.

Glibly one of them said: 'It means that we shall have good houses, and free motorcars and petrol, and free railways and cinemas, and no taxes and no work.'

Another said: 'I know what Socialism is. I used to drive the Zamindar's car. Under Socialism, he will drive mine.'

Part Two

RETURN TO FREE INDIA

4   Back to my People

FOR a number of years, the exigencies of Service took me away from the State. The spinning-wheel turned, and the pitcher was taken to the well, while girls became women and youths became men, before I was able to return to the scenes of my former life.

I was staying in Bombay for two days. Roaming about its busy streets, I came across a small police squad dispersing an aggressive youth rally.

'What's all this about?' I asked an elderly man standing nearby as young fellows walked away, nursing injured heads and jawbones.

'God knows! Frustrations spilling out, I suppose', he replied, shrugging his shoulders.

'Let me speak', interrupted a tall young man to my left who had heard my question. The cut under his left eye and the swollen lip testified that he had been one of the victims of the police melee.

'You just don't understand, sir. The fact is that our present leaders have outlived their day. Like the dinosaur, they should die off, but they refuse to do so. All they can do is to waste time on futile trifles, flogging dead horses and hankering after an India long dead. The new India demands radical changes, which we propose to bring about.'

Then he introduced himself. He was Morgaonkar, a student, deeply interested in Communism as the only solution to India's problems. 'The state of this country is not to be taken lightly', he shouted. 'Leaders here are a lot of dishonest, hypocritical humbugs! Naïve upstarts and cheap publicity hunters, that's what they are! They worship the Mahatma in word, break faith with him in spirit. None of them is any good!'

39

'Leaders and Government officers always are the victims when things go wrong', I replied.

'We want a Government of which we shall be the masters!' he cried defiantly, then disappeared into the crowd.

An hour later, I found myself strolling through the industrial area and, at a tea shop nearby, got into casual conversation with a man called Suresh Mitra. Mitra was a handsome young man with a sparse beard and large deepset eyes. He said he was educated in Calcutta, and had become a mill worker.

'Who says Socialism won't work in India?' he demanded. 'I'll answer for you: the bosses. They are the only ones who do not want to see Socialism work. Don't bother to talk to them about it, but ask the mill hands what they want; they'll tell you they want Socialism. And they want it in a hurry. They want revolution, swift and sweeping! What have these poor people to lose in the battle except their chains?'

He stopped, coughed for several minutes. His spit was flecked with red; it was not the red of pan. The man was ill.

'For Heaven's sake don't waste time trying to plaster and paint the rotten crumbling edifice of civilisation. Tear the damn thing down! build anew! set up Socialism firmly, or not at all. Socialism is not for the timid!'

'My economics are rusty', I said. 'Surely, though, the experts say we should rebuild our social structure gradually.'

'Experts! Bosh!' he snarled. 'Don't fling your bourgeois economics at me! They are patchers, not builders! Socialism can only come explosively. We may create chaos for a short time or for a long time; we may—we will—pass through a phase of dictatorship.... For the sake of our goal, we'll hate, torture, destroy....'

'Your remedy may be worse than the disease.'

'No, no, no!' he screamed. 'We'll stop the exploitation of man by man, sweep away poverty, ignorance, privilege. The common man shall then be supreme; work for peace, ban war.'

'Nonsense! Isn't the common man supreme now?' I retorted. 'World-wide Socialism won't end war. Socialist states will quarrel just as quickly as capitalist states. Look at Russia's ten thousand bombers, and other war material.'

He was on to the fresh scent like a hound in full cry. 'You are mad, I tell you!' he cried in disgust. 'Capitalists and Imperialists, fighting for markets, cause wars; you know it too. They want concessions, spheres of influence, military bases. They want oil. Eliminate the economic rivalries and the causes of war will disappear.'

'And yet the Communists seem to be doing their best to start a war in Asia this very minute', I replied.

'They are not at war with anybody', he yelled, to the delight of the audience we had created in the tea shop. 'They are fighting for the liberation of millions of Asiatic workers from the fangs of Imperialism!' In evident disgust, he glared at me and stormed out of the shop.

It was my last day in Bombay and I was looking round for the changes in my country which had so recently stepped into her freedom. Just as I was thinking of old friends, I suddenly ran into Balwant Rao Joshi. How many things he reminded me of in the long past days of my early service, when I was under him for administrative training. I recalled our forest camps: the intolerable heat; buzzing mosquitoes; the interminable discussions through sleepless nights; the tossing and turning on creaking campcots; the canopy of star-studded skies. Of all these Joshi reminded me. But he also made me realise things were now different from all that we had known. I had always associated Joshi with his well tailored sports jacket and grey flannels, but here he was before me in white cap and dhoti.

'Let alone Western clothes, even a clean colour will raise eyebrows these days! Democracy', he said, 'is responsible for this transformation. Democracy is a process of churning; with the advent of democratic machinery in a backward country a churning up, as it were, starts in society and, in the process, all the dirt comes up. That's how all the undesirable elements with no character or qualifications are pushed to the top and control the Government and the people. The tragedy of it is that they sit in judgment over experienced administrators and consider themselves as the final repositories of wisdom.' There was no attraction now in Government service, complained Joshi.

As we sat in a nearby café, talking of our old times, I was distressed to find that such an able and experienced administrator had no feelings except of disillusionment about the changes taking place. I was not prepared to let this cynicism pass unchallenged; I protested that, while all he said might in a way be true, one had to make a beginning somewhere.

'Perhaps you are right', he said mildly, taking off his white cap and scratching his bald head. 'It may be the price a country must pay, but the fact remains that the mass crushes beneath it everything that is different; everything that is individual, qualified, select.'

'My dear young man', he said gently after a while, sipping his lemonade and with a faint, preoccupied kindness graven on his

41

thin face, 'I trust that these last few years of your life were well spent. Our young men have been heavily occupied all this time with many pressing problems and with the clashes and heartbreaks these problems have brought in their wake. Partition, communalism, provincialism, unemployment, economic unrest, incapacity of the Government, all have taken their toll of life and fortune in India.'

I was not in a mood for any heavy discussion and he obviously sensed it. When asked how his two sons Govind and Vithal were, he said: 'Both graduated three years ago but, with all their efforts, they are still unable to get jobs. It is hard nowadays to find employment anywhere unless, of course, you have powerful godfathers.'

Smiling, he added with a fleeting expression of shy self-reproach, 'In fact, I was on my way to see an old friend who is trying to arrange a match for Govind. If he succeeds Govind may be engaged to the daughter of the party boss. At least his problem may be solved.'

We promised to meet again. I walked quietly away.

The next day I left by air for South India to see old friends and, if possible, to visit some of the villages where I had worked years before. That summer morning from my seat next to the window near the front of the plane I could scan the countryside. Below us, as though it were some tiny string which had slipped off a giant's package, ran a metalled highway through a barren countryside. We cruised along for some time and, looking again directly below, I saw a domed hill with trunks of trees strewn on it like matches thrown casually on an ant-hill, perhaps remnants of a forest fire. We flew over hills and dirt roads and dry streams. Just off one dirt road, near a drying reservoir of water, were two decrepit and unplanned villages consisting mostly of mud houses. My thoughts were suddenly diverted to the vast multitudes that inhabit those thousands of similar villages where the real India lives and toils. I was unable to read with comfort and, as I could not sleep, I was soon lost in thinking. I thought of the future of those teeming millions of half-starved and scantily clothed people and of the obstacles to their progress and prosperity. They have a primitive economy embedded in ignorance. People in similar circumstances in Russia had to be dragged by the scruff of the neck to salvation. Or was it salvation? Was it true that the new order there was only attained at the price of freedom? If so, are we to pay with our freedom for the bread, clothes and shelter our people so desperately need?

42

I thought of the road which the British were travelling, but was it not the product of a long educative process? Had not democracy been interwoven with their history for hundreds of years? What is the use of improving men's material condition, I thought, unless we give them spiritual freedom also? We do not want an India populated by a race of plump, healthy slaves! But then political liberty is worthless if one is too poor to enjoy it. Political liberty and economic reforms, I felt certain, should go hand in hand if we, as a nation, are to emerge into the green uplands of prosperity.

I thought again of British efforts to give social security and a fair distribution of wealth through democratic processes and of the way they had kept intact the main bastions of freedom, a free press and freedom to criticise Government how and when they liked. If we preserved the basic freedoms, a Socialist Government could go no further than the people wished, yet if prosperity was to come only through gradual change, how long would it take us to reach the goal?

The crux of any political reform, I felt sure, is to reconcile the rights of the individual with the needs of society; and any planned economic system must satisfy the latter, but not at the expense of the former. The same problem, it appeared to me, baffled international relations: the conflict between the rights of the individual nation and the world's need for peace. With these thoughts I dozed off and was awakened by the plane's touching down at my destination.

Hyder, with whom I was to stay, lived some distance outside the city in a sort of colony of his friends and relations. He was light brown, in his late fifties, with kind and lively eyes. He was a blend of Moghul feudal culture and English Victorian tradition. He lived in a place where feudal court life had survived into the mid-twentieth century, and where also there had been a succession of British administrators who belonged more to the age of Clive and Warren Hastings than that of Irwin and Mountbatten. Here the civil servant had been born into a feudal hierarchy, but brought up under the paternal care of the British administrator. The result was Hyder: loyal to his tap-roots but hankering after the glamour and the enchantment which seemed to have gone for ever.

The political struggles in the country and the advent of the new Government were both a crisis and a tragedy for Hyder. Here were events that not only had severed the British connection he loved and respected so much, but had also destroyed his own roots nearer home. It was a double blow which Hyder

43

could neither withstand nor understand. All he could see and feel was a growing resentment within himself, a vague awareness of falling standards, of failing efficiency, a cheap attempt at catering to the wishes of the mob, playing to the gallery, instead of a purposive and constructive canalisation of energies. All this made Hyder's disappointment take the air of disillusionment and in time he began even to grow righteous about it. In his days, administration had been an exclusive matter, far from the madding crowd. There had been a sense of direction; the machinery had been geared to a purpose and every cog in that machine was aware of its place in that larger purpose. Not everyone had, of course, a clear conception of that purpose, but everyone had a sense of belonging. Administration was for the most part efficient and clean; it moved majestically and purposefully towards a goal. Today all this was no more. Uneducated men with neither breeding nor character had control of the administration; their sole purpose was to divide the spoils among themselves and to keep others sufficiently in humour to assure their own success in the next election.

Hyder was not bitter; he was too well bred for bitterness. But he was sorry; sorry for them, not for himself. For himself he had no need to be sorry. He was an intelligent man and he had sensed much earlier that his age and his way of living could not survive for long. He was not, therefore, taken by surprise by the march of events. He gracefully retired. To his children he had given a professional education and they were all well placed, sheltered from the political vagaries of the country. They were in British firms; the British were both shrewd and grateful. They knew that the sons of men like Hyder would be their best and most loyal employees in these changing times. They deliberately recruited only such young men, men with a family background and breeding. And Hyder was both glad and grateful. To him it was more than a job for a son; it was the fulfilment of a lifetime of faith in that race of 'Heaven born'. This act of recognition helped him save one last citadel of faith at least at a time when all his life-long beliefs had been swept away by the tide of affairs, by the common touch of common men. His sons at least had been saved from the flood, and that was a just tribute to his foresight.

'These levelling doctrines', he said one night after dinner, as he paced up and down his veranda, tightly encased in his long dove-grey achkan, 'give those who preach them a sort of religious fervour. Nature knows no equality. With a grossly uneven hand, she distributes health, beauty, strength, intelligence

44

... all the gifts which make one man superior or inferior to his fellow. Isn't it absurd, then, to talk of equality?' He continued after a pause: 'I do not mean by equality identity of treatment. I recognise the infinite variety of human personality; we need, accordingly, to give it the most diverse means of expression. But you have a national society in which men live so differently and have no common ideology binding them together. They do not share in a common idea; they do not strive towards a common goal. They lack that fundamental unity of purpose which gives vigour and tenacity to the national life.'

Said Farida, his wife: 'They mean equality of opportunity.'

'Equality of opportunity', he said in a tone somewhat raised, 'is perhaps an equal opportunity to prove unequal talents.' And then he added after a pause: 'They have tacitly scrapped that equality by giving varying rates of pay, just as do the capitalists; and with inequality of income comes inequality of opportunity.'

'What they mean', said Farida, 'is an equal chance for everyone to develop to the fullest of his or her ability.'

'Why do Socialists always have to explain that Marx didn't really mean what he said? Is this "equal chance" enough? Doesn't it leave too much to the "law of the jungle"? To insist on equal chances is merely to hold the ring for the economic struggle.'

'The task', I said, 'of democracy is to get the best out of every man without reference to the religion, caste, race or fortune of himself or his parents. The son of a blacksmith should be able to become a Prime Minister, and the son of a Prime Minister a blacksmith, if that is what he is best suited for.'

'These are platitudes', said Hyder. 'There is nothing new in these ideas, but they have been found impracticable even in the Soviet Union. There, Socialism is just a planned economy under state ownership, with no equal share in the result.'

Farida said: 'The difficulty is to combine liberty with efficiency, especially with the progress of the mind and the spirit through education, so that true equality may develop.'

Hyder laid his hand affectionately on hers. 'My dear', he said, 'you are the living refutation of your own words for, by God, you have no equal!'

Farida laughed, pleased. 'Don't waste time flattering an old woman', she said.

'The trouble with these apostles of equality', said Hyder, 'is that they are so negative. They think that between them and prosperity stand only a few people like us. But you cannot lift the wage-earner by pulling down the wage-payer nor strengthen the weak by weakening the strong. You cannot help the poor by destroying the rich, nor build character and courage by killing all initiative and independence.'

'Do you then believe in aristocracy?' I asked.

'Certainly, if its privileges are derived from intellect and character. I see nothing sacred in democracy which is based on the mistaken notion of equality. The coolie in the field is *not* my equal and, even if we had been brought up in precisely similar circumstances, we should still have grown up no more equal than the thoroughbred racehorse and the tonga pony. Why then should they have, by virtue of mere numbers, immensely greater power than I?'

I thought, as I watched his nervous walk, how much he resembled a fine racehorse. It was indeed absurd to think of his being relegated to the shafts of a tonga.

'Therefore', Hyder continued, 'democracy has failed. Yet nobody in his senses would recommend a return to the aristocracy of birth which we idealised in our caste system.'

'What is your solution then?'

'Politicians propose to change men from without, by social and political means. I want to change them from within.'

'By religious revival?'

'No. By science. The whole trend of your social democracy is a glorification of brawn over brain, of the hand over the head, of emotion over reason. Therefore the democratic state comes to be run by mediocre men, office-seekers, climbers of little ability but much personal ambition, especially in our country, which is ruled largely by hordes of low-grade men dragging down others to their own level. The survival of the least fit, perhaps', he said with an impish chuckle. 'We must produce better men if we want to build a better world.'

'Supermen?' I asked.

'By no means. But we should decide with human beings, just as we do with horses or grade cattle, which should and which should not reproduce their species. It is the only way in which the breed of men can be improved.'

'I don't think that is at all a good idea', said Farida. 'Where would our fine sons be if the Government had disapproved of you?'

Hyder's point of view was echoed with peculiar emphasis by his cousin Mumtaz, Uncle Mumtaz to all of us in the old days.

'As the honourable Minister ascended the platform his legs were exposed through a rather scanty dhoti.' That was Mumtaz's

46

chief complaint against democracy. Not that Mumtaz objected to the exposure of legs as such—he always looked avidly at Marlene Dietrich on the screen—but except for the degree of exposure there was no other similarity in the two cases. Mumtaz was about fifty years of age. He had a thatch of greying hair on a large square head. He had aristocratic looks and a perfect set of teeth. With his background Mumtaz could not adjust himself to the changed times, nor did he think such an attempt was called for or was even worthwhile. He resented the change very much with a resentment which took the shape of a continuous smouldering bitterness against the new set-up and the new men in power. Mumtaz's ideas of administration were different. He had been an efficient officer once; he felt he could never be that again. A man could not be efficient when he was not trusted, and Mumtaz felt he was not trusted now. Further, in this set-up where any man walking in the street felt competent to judge administrative matters and had the opportunities to make his opinion count, there would be no place for Mumtaz.

He was neither a nobleman nor a feudal lord when he entered Government service; he was only one of the upper middle class. But once in service, he brought to life an air of superiority and exclusiveness appropriate to the outlook of a real blue-blooded nobleman. He felt a passionate loyalty to the State. He served it with a ruthlessness which was neither demanded nor indeed required. He divided his existence into two water-tight compartments, one of cold efficiency and the other of unbridled, almost licentious, enjoyment. He was a social success: people still remembered his old, outrageous parties to which he always welcomed friends and friends' friends. None of his many guests could forget that beautiful house on the hillock, the scene of such uproarious nights in Mumtaz's heyday.

Yet Uncle Mumtaz had been, as I have related, very efficient. He had kept his whole jurisdiction under his thumb. His strong sense of loyalty could tolerate nothing opposed to the welfare of the Raj. The welfare of the people apart from that of the Raj had meant nothing to him. His entire faith in the future of the Raj had given him courage to be ruthless. When, therefore, political events suddenly changed the order of things, Uncle Mumtaz was taken by surprise; he had no time to adjust himself. Overnight, he found his erstwhile zeal and loyalty denounced as cruelty and subversion. Uncle Mumtaz was never an intellectual. He was a man of emotions and passions. The change led him sometimes to philosophise. He was bitter against the new order. To him democracy was only mob-rule; the new leaders

47

were power-mad dacoits who humoured the scum of the earth and seized office for their own ends. What had these new times to offer? There was not a single officer in the service with the efficiency of Uncle Mumtaz. These upstart clerks, petty pleaders, agitators and windbags could not be administrators. Nobody had a faith today and nobody was really loyal. They all preached morality like Victorian grandmothers, but what were their own lives like? Lives of hypocrisy and hidden voice! Uncle Mumtaz at least felt no obligation to anyone. He had worked hard; he paid for what he got and no favours were asked or given. But today: these men wanted to enjoy life without paying for it. Somebody had to pay for it all; and so all these upstarts had lost not only their virtue but also their independence: result, nepotism! And what could administration be without independent and upright officers?

And so Uncle Mumtaz gloated complacently over the evils of today. He would never admit that his age had passed, that his faith had failed him. The only consolation which he could find for his own disintegration was the conviction that other people had become degraded. He could not see in change the inevitable march of time, the working of historical forces, the unfolding of a new era of greater concern for the greater number. To him the expression 'brute majority' was a magical formula which undermined both the logical necessity and the moral validity of democracy. Yet there was some excuse for his cynicism. For whatever else it may or may not have destroyed, this new Government by majority had certainly destroyed the economic warp and woof of his own family life. Mumtaz's family, like many others, had depended solely on Government service; in fact this had gone on for so long that his kinsfolk as they grew up felt that Government jobs would come as inevitably to them as did their children. This being so, he, like many others of his community, fathered an indiscreetly large family. And suddenly the whole traditional pattern was upset. He himself was obliged to retire; his income was halved. Of his two brothers, one was dismissed from the service and the other left for Pakistan immediately after Partition as a jobless refugee, leaving his entire family behind. His elder son, who had been in a temporary department, had been 'retrenched'. So every one of the family now had to live on Mumtaz's pension. And that was not all. Many distant and mysterious relatives began turning up, who had all lost their jobs, their lands and their means of livelihood; who all thought Mumtaz's pension was big enough for anything. Mumtaz's wife formerly drew a handsome hereditary cash grant every month;

this also stopped. While the total income of the household was dwindling, these hosts of relatives showed no frugality, no initiative, no appreciation, not even common sense. They looked to Government service or nothing, because they were not fitted for anything else. None was willing to try any fresh avenue of employment, even if it appeared available. All demanded khichri (fried rice) and khima (fried minced meat) for breakfast, a heavy lunch and an even heavier dinner. No wonder Mumtaz was sometimes bitter at the changes which had overtaken his condition. Yet bitterness solves no problem. In all this cloud of misfortune the silver lining was that two of his nephews at least, who were in the Army, had stood fast and made good. These two favourite nephews had once fought side by side in Africa and Italy. Now they faced each other, one in the Pakistan Army and one in the Indian Army.

'If war comes', said Uncle Mumtaz, on one of our evening walks, 'it will not be because Munsoor and Azam hate each other, nor even because the peoples of India and Pakistan thirst for each other's blood. It will be through sheer helplessness, through the inability to check the juggernaut which has been set in motion by national pride and is kept going by national propaganda.'

'You and others, Uncle', I said, somewhat impatiently, 'keep on talking of a change of heart, of the need for moral regeneration. But where does that get us? What we want is a practical policy which will get us out of our difficulties soon.'

The hill here was steep for him, but when he had reached the top and recovered his breath, he contin.ed: 'Practical policy? Moral regeneration is the most practical step you can imagine. Nations are very much like individuals. When all nations know themselves and judge themselves, then, and only then, will World Government be possible. Till then, they will blame fate and other nations for their own failure. The oldest trick of Governments is to distract the citizens' attention by inciting them against a foreign foe. "Stand united!" "Show a bold front!" "Tighten your belts! ... The enemy is at the gates!" Then any opposition becomes treachery, any criticism treason. You will find that the worse the economic situation gets, the more heroic and determined any Government will be in its foreign affairs.'

'I often feel', I said, 'that with all our progress and civilisation we don't know where we are going and we don't really care.'

'To travel hopefully is better than to arrive.' He stopped again to draw breath. 'Has the growth of our spiritual life kept pace with all the technical and scientific achievements? Has not our whole spiritual existence, rather, become mechanised?

49

And aren't human beings sometimes worse than beasts? The fact is that we are dehumanising ourselves—the modern man assesses his own value and that of his fellow men by technical standards alone.'

'Is culture possible? Is there any hope?' I asked.

'Culture can be and is inherited; civilisation is always acquired and learnt. . . . Culture is an attribute of the spirit of man and his effort to assert its inner and independent being. . . . We think of the world, of humanity, but never of individuals. If the individual is at peace and is happy, if he has tolerance and the desire to help his fellow beings, the world problem ceases to exist. Peace will only come when there is understanding, where there is confidence in oneself.'

While I was staying with Hyder, his son Humayoon came for a few 'days' visit. He was a sailor, a burly, brawny young man with sleepy good looks and thoughtful brown eyes. He had seen battle with the Navy and, since the end of the war, had sailed the seven seas. He had nothing of the father's fine-drawn nervous intellect; but his father's forethought had given him what is more valuable nowadays—professional training and technical knowledge. These, allied to his inherited self-confidence and aptitude for command, made him a fine officer. One meets all too few Indians who have travelled widely with their eyes and ears open, and I felt that he and I belonged to a free-masonry from which the others were excluded.

'You have called at ports in Eastern Europe', I said. 'You must have peeped behind the Iron Curtain. Tell me what you saw.'

Humayoon shrugged his shoulders. 'Yes, certainly. There is as much poverty in many parts of these countries as in India, and a lowering threatening suspicion such as we have never known in this country, Alhamdu'lillah!'

'Wait and see', I said. 'You have only just come home.'

'So far', said Humayoon, 'from freeing man from toil and want, Socialism makes him work harder for less. The trouble with the Marxists is their intolerable conceit, their flinty rigidity. If Marx said that black was white, they'd go round whitewashing every black object they could find and excommunicate any heretic who hinted that the prophet was perhaps mistaken.'

'Lenin said that to reject compromise is childish.'

'I don't care what Lenin said. I've seen what his disciples do. Isn't that enough?'

'The Iron Curtain countries may be Socialist, but democratic they are not. Perhaps the faults you see are the faults of auto-cracy, not of Socialism.'

'Are you a Socialist, Rihaz Bhai?'

'I don't know. But I am sure that no economic system ought to be evolved by the planners without the co-operation of the planned. And I believe that policies should be moulded by reason, not by passion. The idea that reform can only come violently is begotten by envy out of despair.'

'Perhaps you admire Socialism but despise Socialists', Huma-yoon said with a twinkle in his eye.

'It is curious', I said; 'the hall-mark of progressive thought today is the glorification of the primitive, a worship of the mythical past. Our reformers urge us on to the New Age, with nostalgic backward glances. They insist on calling India "Bharat", and the Central Provinces "Madhya Pradesh". One hand points to the Marxist paradise, the other back to the jungle.'

Hyder came into the room smoking his after-dinner cigar. 'What a fellow you are for politics, Rihaz', he said. 'I want to hear about Humayoon's seafaring.'

'We were discussing', I said, 'the present transitional stage between ...'

'Then don't talk about it as if it were something abnormal. History is an endless chain of transitions. Get it into your head that transition is the only permanency. The one remarkable thing about our transition is that it is guided by dreamers and Jacks-in-office.'

'Socialism can work all right', I said, 'given the proper human material.'

'So can any "ism". But the material necessary for Socialism does not exist in our country today.'

Hyder's old friend, Asif, lives in a strange house, partly carved out of solid rock. Once he enjoyed power as well as wealth; now he has some of his ancestral wealth left, but there is no place for him in public administration. So he broods too much, and is becoming bitter and cynical for lack of the work and responsi-bility which were the breath of life to him. His family is noble, with a long and honourable tradition of service. But the tumult-uous changes of recent times only bewilder him. He took no stance in political manoeuvres in his younger days, nor did he under-stand them. He always stood solidly for certain moral values, such as honesty, generosity and gentleness in human dealings; his complaint against our times is that these values are being lost, and, as a consequence, he has become a cynic. It never occurs to him that his attachment to these virtues may be not unconnected with his position as a rich nobleman who can afford to be virtuous. A gentleman himself, he expects everyone to be the same, especially if they are men of birth and breeding like his own. Of course, he is disappointed.

The first impact of politics on administration, it appeared, had left Asif merely bewildered. But when, along with politics, raging passions also influenced administration, when common men brought their common hates and vices to it, Asif gently withdrew from public life. He has never been one for the thick of any battle. Despite all his cynicism, he believes and practises the gentler virtues of life. He says that when he himself was an administrator, administration was not the Temple of Mammon it now is; it was a fine and noble profession. You dealt with only a few other noble souls like yourself; you worked with honesty and integrity; with loyalty to the Ruler and for the common good of the people. What this meant is not now relevant; those days are gone. Now administration has become the main arena for political battles. Asif found no place in it and he retired gracefully.

Asif could retire because his job had never been anything but a hobby. Since men must not sit idle, he had decided to work. When work became debasing, he could cease to do it. In all his goodness it never occurred to Asif to ask himself whether all others could answer the problems of life so easily.

'It is nice', he said in a voice quiet and gentle, 'to see you again. Now that I am out of favour, most of my friends find my house rather inaccessible. I hear you have changed and turned philosopher.'

'It is only in novels that people suddenly change. In real life we remain much the same.'

He poured out a drink and looked surprised when I declined it. 'You really don't drink? What did you do in Europe? Your education is incomplete.'

'I am still a barbarian', I said.

'Life is short, my friend, and there is nothing beyond it. So why not make the most of it?'

He half-filled the glass with whisky and splashed in some soda. 'Do you believe in survival after death?'

'I believe there is a flame in us that never dies. We increase or diminish it according to the way we live. Man is born with a chance of survival.'

'Ah, a common fallacy', said Asif. 'You see, there are really only four doctrines: the pursuit of unselfishness or doing good to others; the pursuit of selfishness or seeking one's own good; the pursuit of God, or mysticism; and the pursuit of beauty. That is all. There is nothing else. Men in all ages have chosen one of these or a mixture of them. There may be some truth in each of them, but in the ultimate analysis we remain ourselves. It is our own life that we must lead, our own goal which we must seek. At the end of everything we remain alone, of ourselves, by ourselves, for ourselves. Life is a lonely journey to a lonely destination.'

I was quite taken aback by his words. As he reached for his second glass of whisky his face seemed to grow gentler and softer. There was something appealing about his manner of speaking.

'Are you, then', I asked, 'an apostle of selfishness?'

'By no means', said Asif. 'The trouble with us is that we take ourselves much too seriously. All that we need is to do our best at the thing we are doing and bother others as little as possible. Do not expect Utopia; it will never come. Mind your own business and enjoy life as best you can. You will serve the world best by getting what you want and resting content with that. All the trouble in the world is caused by discontented men, the reformers, the idealists, the men who wish to do good and better the lot of their fellow-creatures.'

'That is one way of looking at life', I said, 'Safety first.'

'No, take any risk, if you think your happiness depends on it.'

I asked after a pause: 'Is there anything like justice and virtue in human affairs, Asif?'

He smiled, the smile of a cynic. 'Justice', he said, 'is what Government does.'

He lit a cigarette and continued: 'You see, men invent myths to rationalise and justify their conduct. What is virtue? It is only an offshoot of vanity, the habit of acting in a manner which others praise. Half the harm that is done in this world is due to people who want to feel important and virtuous.'

I thought his wife, Shamim, had not been listening; but she looked up from her needlework and said: 'Pay no attention to him whatever, Rihaz. He is the kindest and the most unselfish man in all the world.'

As luck would have it, the next man I visited was one of the sort who had displaced Asif from power. The Honourable Minister upon whom I called is a new phenomenon in the state machinery: a man who embodies in his own person the new fashionable idea that the technique of administration is mere child's play to anyone who has climbed to authority on the political ladder.

I had taken pains to find out something of the Minister's history. He had started as Anjiah Patel of half a dozen villages and in due course became middle-aged, worldly-wise, a landlord and a vakil (pleader), a not unusual combination. Although qualified as a vakil class III, he never practised in the courts, but employed his legal knowledge to make life miserable for anyone who tried to oppose him. By sharp dealings and by using his farm servants as private police and strong-arm men, he increased his influence and position year by year. Very early in his career he had realised the importance of keeping in the good books of anyone powerful enough to injure or help him; he cringed before all the officials who toured the area, lavishly bribing the subordinates to ensure that complaints against his behaviour were suppressed before they came to the notice of the officials. To keep important visitors sweet he practised lavish hospitality, maintaining a kind of free guest-house for anyone likely to be useful to him. One day he received a call from a prominent popular politician who was touring an area usually considered remote and backward on the off-chance of discovering grievances which could be exploited politically. Anjiah and the politician had long discussions together; a bargain was struck. Anjiah promised to use his local influence and money when required by the political bosses. The politician promised that no awkward questions would be raised about how Anjiah ruled his little domain and the way he was amassing his fortune.

This was Anjiah's introduction to politics.

As more and more political organisers came to stay with him and enjoy his hospitality, which included presents in the guise of contributions to political funds, Anjiah's ambition spread its wings. He was wealthy; he had had an unchallengeable local position. Was he not every bit as good as those leaders whose names were well-known all over the State? Why should he not become a leader himself? The only thing necessary was that he should become known in a wider sphere. Soon the opportunity came. Officials, concerned with the internal security of the State, began to cast a suspicious eye on Anjiah's new political friends. Anjiah decided that it would suit his purpose to go and live for some time outside the State in a city where he had some friends. Amply supplied with funds, he began to entertain his friends, associating daily with the leaders, and cultivating the local press so that his name was printed along with theirs in reports of all political gatherings. Soon he came to be regarded as a leader himself, although whom he led, and whether he led them, nobody seemed to know or wanted to know.

There was one further qualification which he needed: a short term of imprisonment for political activity. This he achieved, painlessly and satisfactorily, by taking part in a public demonstration which the authorities had forbidden, thus earning a comparatively short sentence.

He now entered the wider stage of State politics and with his wealth, capacity for manipulation and self-assurance, he was so well recognised as a 'public leader' that he was nominated a Minister. He learned, parrot-wise, a series of slogans about the virtues of Mahatma Gandhi's saintly struggle for *Purna Swaraj*; the wickedness of British rule; the glories of ancient India; the future that was going to be like the ancient past. Endowed with a loud voice and a confident, even truculent, manner, he began to address meetings himself. He abandoned his old name in favour of a more dignified appellation; he threw himself with fervour into speech-making and oratory and secret meetings of his friends. Elections were not far away; his tentative position had now to be made regular. He took two precautions; he was shrewd enough to know that success depended on his money and wire-pulling He spent money freely; many small presents and larger promises secured the support of other and less successful Anjiah Patels in the constituency for which he desired to stand after the Constitution came into force. Wire-pulling and loudly advertised 'sacrifices', which he was supposed to have made in the cause of independence, secured him nomination as an approved candidate, that is to say, the backing of the bosses. Of course, he needed no political programme; his set of slogans served him well. Didn't the people know that he had gone to prison in the fight for freedom? It might have been a very short sentence, but even so. ... Didn't they know he would put down firmly what was remaining of the old 'blood-suckers'?

The Honourable Minister's first act after his elevation to the position was to earmark for his official residence a magnificent palace formerly belonging to a nobleman. Accompanied by a confidential clerk (who had in former days served me in the same capacity and from whom I had the tale), the Honourable Minister started exploring the new house. Entering a sumptuous bathroom, he decided to impress his clerk with his acquaintance with modern plumbing, some of the mysteries of which he had fathomed from his experience of trains and hotels. To pull a chain and to release a flood of water was the work of an instant; the

55

clerk was duly awed. But close by stood another contraption, like a small low bath, in blue porcelain : a bidet.

'What is that, sir?' asked the clerk.

The Minister did not know; he had never seen the like before. But he would never admit his ignorance to a subordinate.

'I'll show you', he said, as he advanced upon it boldly and turned a shining tap. Alas, a vertical jet of water sprang up to take him full in the face. The Minister became speechless with fury. Who would have expected a concealed fountain in such a place? From that moment dated his great discovery, a discovery which set the pattern of his political career, that Western civilisation and all its trappings were completely irrational, unworthy of imitation by free India.

Slipping into or slipping out of official national costume, the constricting churidar and achkan, was a terrible job and the Honourable Minister found that he had to employ considerable energy in doing this; still he never reflected how much more difficult it was to slip so suddenly into or out of a new way of living, but this was exactly what he had done, and what his rustic friends hanging around him were desperately trying to do.

The Honourable Minister had a very peculiar attitude towards the old order. He abused it vehemently; he spoke of the former bureaucracy as if it had been a gangrenous growth. Yet, deep down in his heart, his real ambition was always to step into the shoes of that bureaucracy. To begin with, liveried servants (it did not matter, and he did not care, if the liveries were dirty and torn); next, a flag on the car and a police guard at the main gate of his residence. It was now his ambition to do all that the old bureaucracy (as he thought) had done; it became almost an obsession with him. He and his friends wanted to behave exactly like the very class they had thrown out. And so the Honourable Minister fretted and fumed, yet insisted in putting on an achkan and a churidar while attending formal functions, although at home and elsewhere he always wore his dhoti.

He knew little and cared less about administering his Department, spending all his time intriguing with or against his colleagues to make himself secure and to increase his own importance, making sure that his name appeared in the local dailies. He applied to every matter which came before him officially the simple principle of somehow turning it to the advantage of himself and of those who supported him. He treated all the officials in his Department like defaulters, lecturing them, bullying them, shouting at them, as though he were prosecuting criminals. Of course, he often transferred them from post to post at the behest of his helpers and friends.

I made an appointment to see him.

As I entered the compound, I saw the police guard, which consisted of three constables who were smoking so comfortably that they scarcely troubled to take notice of me as I passed. The garden, which had once been among the great beauties of the palace, was overgrown and neglected; the unmown lawns were piled high with empty packing cases. That the new owner of the residence had taken great pains to introduce into it the comfortable disorder of his village home was glaringly obvious. Nails had been driven into the finely-carved stonework of the portico to support strings of withered mango leaves; the marble floor of the entrance was smeared with coloured patterns. In one part of the side veranda with the pierced marble tracery, buffaloes were tied up, dragging their fodder from the blue porcelain bidet which had once aroused the Minister's wrath—no doubt removed from the bathroom to serve this useful purpose.

A servant in dirty livery ushered me into a sitting room which I remembered as the study of the former owner of the house. The solid furniture was there, as in the old days, but how sadly changed. Tapestried chairs were covered with dirt and grease, the sofas were filthy with stains of hair oil and muddy shoes, the carpet was almost in rags and littered with bits of paper, empty cigarette cartons and even discarded footwear. Round the walls, crowded and at uneven heights, hung advertising calendars along with cheap bazaar prints of national heroes in tawdry tinsel frames, each bearing a dusty, fly-blown garland of faded artificial flowers. Gandhiji, Jawaharlal Nehru, Subhas Bose, looked down disapprovingly upon this squalid disorder, every detail of which was uncompromisingly revealed by the glare of enormous fluorescent lights of the type favoured by cheaper cafés and restaurants.

The servant reappeared after a short time and carefully conducted me to the Minister's study. This was the main banqueting hall, an enormous apartment suitable only for ceremonial occasions. The Minister's desk, a standard Public Works Department production with a stained green baize top, stood incongruously in the middle of an acre of uncarpeted boards. Another portrait gallery of bazaar prints and laudatory 'addresses' presented to him in the towns he visited, in even more gaudy frames, graced the walls, interspersed with cheap oleographs of gods and goddesses in glaring colours which, as in the sitting room, bore faded garlands of paper flowers. A few office chairs were scattered about; but the object which held my attention was a vast dressing table in walnut, complete with a looking glass, which the Minister plainly considered a highly appropriate piece of furniture for his private sanctuary. Had someone told him, I wondered, that all palaces ought to be furnished with mirrors? No doubt he liked the looking glass because it reflected so splendidly the blinding glare of the fluorescent lighting which, here too, was in full blaze.

The Minister did not come forward to meet me but heaved his now bulging body half out of his chair as I approached. He shouted a greeting in a voice as loud as if I had been a quarter of a mile away, and then sank back behind the desk. I looked curiously at the objects on the desk top. There was an expensive desk set of fountain pens in front of the official blotting pad, flanked by three tarnished brass bowls. One contained the Minister's artificial teeth; the other, perhaps, a carton of digestion tablets; the third held a few rusty pins and paper fasteners. A tall brass vase containing artificial flowers stood on top of some departmental files which, like everything else on the desk, were so heavily coated with dust that they could not have been read for a long time.

The Honourable Minister looked between sixty-five and seventy but, since he was born before births were formally registered, he was accustomed to add or subtract years whenever it suited his purpose. When a public demand for 'younger Ministers' was voiced, he loudly proclaimed that he would not hold office for a day after he had attained the age of sixty. But it was whispered that this was a perfectly safe promise to make, because the moment when it became due for fulfilment would be determined solely by himself.

The Honourable Minister leaned across the table towards me in a confidential way. His heavily-starched yellow khadder shirt crackled (he would never wear soft white khadder—it was far too commonplace and would not show how convinced a follower of Gandhiji he was).

Like everybody else, he expressed time and again, during our preliminary conversation, warm admiration for Nehru. He felt, however, that Nehru's non-communalism was his blind spot; and that in this matter he knew better. He hated Nehru's occasional open attacks on communalism and provincialism as they always left him with a feeling that they were directed against him personally.

It was all very well to talk of a secular state, he argued, but every dog should have his day and it was now the day of the erstwhile oppressed. Somewhat unexpectedly, he interjected :

'We want men like you, Rihaz Sahib.'

Until I could collect myself to reply to this flattering compliment, I tried a new tack and talked to him of unity as the great need of the hour. I told him how thinking on lines of language, sect, caste, religious beliefs, cuts across the very fundamentals of our national life. I particularly mentioned the sad revival of comunal disorders whose roots, in my view, were so deeply embedded in the medieval compost of religious hatreds.

He broke into my talk rapidly, drumming on the desk with his thick fingers.

'I don't trouble myself about all that', he said. 'I leave it all to my good friend Panditji, who knows all about religious impartiality. I have to take a practical view. Our party has gone to the top and we mean to stay there.' He winked at me.

Next to Gandhi's, Nehru's name could end any argument in our country and so I thought it best to change the subject once again, for after all, I did not want to embarrass the man. As to how far Nehru was followed was a different matter. And so I asked: 'Do tell me, Mantriji, what you are trying to achieve here? What is your aim?'

Promptly came the reply—so promptly that I knew it would take the form of some catch word often used. 'A co-operative commonwealth', he said proudly.

'And what is that, exactly?'

'Oh, a society where all wealth belongs to the commonwealth.'

'How will you do this?'

'Very simply; there will be many co-operative societies.'

I gaped with astonishment.

He added, after a pause: 'Yes, even the capitalist will hold his capital as a trustee, a trustee appointed by God. That is what Gandhiji taught us.'

That appeared to leave no room for further talk and I took my leave.

5 The Impact of Communism

AT last, after more than four years, I was going back to the villages where I had spent the happy early years of my service. On that April day I caught the early morning train. Six hours I spent in a rickety carriage, passing through a depressing landscape of dry fields. We had a few minutes' halt after every 30 miles or so, when we would be importuned by whining wrecks of humanity begging for food with incessant and pathetic cries of 'Oh Baba, Oh Sahib!' Most of these were children with dirty matted hair and emaciated bodies clad only in rags.

I had two companions in the compartment. As is the custom when travelling in India, we soon became acquainted. The older of the two, Shahid Ali, a slight, stooping, grey-haired man in his early fifties, was a lawyer. The other man, Nageswar Rao, was a lecturer at a local College. He looked the part.

'Where did you say you were bound?' asked Nageswar Rao.

'I shall be getting down at Karammet station', I replied.

'I wouldn't if I were you', said Shahid Ali. 'What takes you there? The whole area is infested with Communists and every train has a police or military bodyguard. Didn't you see them at the last station?'

'Yes, but I never connected them with Communists.'

'It is hell there. The Reds have spread themselves all over, terrorising everybody and playing ducks and drakes with life and property.'

'A few years ago I worked in that area', I commented, 'and I should like to see things now for myself. They used to be good people.'

'Then you must prepare yourself for unpleasant surprises. You are dealing with Communists, who are bereft of all feelings.'

'I have had to suffer', broke in Rao. 'They burnt my school building and accused me of arson.' As though it might have been an afterthought, he added: 'You should make arrangements for a police escort: you'll need one.'

'Do you know this area?' asked Shahid Ali. 'I am going to Karammet to represent some clients in court; and I assure you that I'm not staying there an hour more than I need to. I have a lot of clients in the area and I hear what goes on', he added.

'But I knew the area intimately in the old days', I said. 'Such peaceful, pleasant people. I can hardly connect them with the tales of cruelty and violence I now hear.'

'Believe me', said Shahid Ali, 'you have not heard half the truth. And all these terrible things are done by those who were once decent, kindly people. You see, for thirty years we have been fanning the embers of communal hatred, undermining the authority of Government and the rule of law, spreading cynicism and scandals about our rulers: all this with the deliberate intention of teaching the people to hate the Government and to blame it for all their sufferings. Now the chickens have come home to roost. It is like a train out of control, racing downhill, and not even the engine driver, Nehru, can stop it; and God knows there is nobody fit to take over from him!'

'So you blame pre-Independence agitation for all this, do you?' I remarked casually.

'Well', he answered after a pause, 'I speak in general terms, but in these districts it is particularly bad. We are reverting to barbarism; the erstwhile followers of Gandhi, paying lip service to non-violence, will pluck out the eyes of policemen, drive nails into the soles of Customs Inspectors' feet, loot banks and murder the guards, and would even assassinate Gandhi himself, all in the name of the masses and all for the sake of the motherland.'

'I cannot agree with you', said Rao with some heat. 'God knows my family and I have suffered as much as any from these disorders, but it is grossly unfair to attribute the crimes of a few thousand ruffians to the idealists who won us our freedom. Why did you cry out for freedom, if you don't like it when you have it?'

Said Shahid Ali: 'We wanted to do away with our former masters at any cost and we believed that the end justified the means. But what is the result? There is chaos in this part of the State, an increase in mutual ill-will and savage communal passions.'

'What is actually happening?' I asked. 'How is it being

tackled by the Government? Is there, in fact, a Communist organisation in each one of these villages?'

'Well, in the first place', said Shahid Ali, 'in some parts of the country Government authority extends no further than the range of the troops who have been posted there. Except in garrison centres, Government is merely ignored. The peasants are seizing all the lands and are refusing to pay rents or taxes. The ring-leaders raise their own taxes and sometimes run their own courts.'

'Who are these ring-leaders?'

'Just gangs of local ruffians.'

'Are these people chosen by popular vote?'

'My dear friend, you must get out of your head the idea that this anarchy has anything to do with accepted political theory. These ignorant people, who are very poor, have turned to banditry for a living. It is just a smash-and-grab raid; smash the landowner, the Bania, the Patwari, and grab their property. Of course, all public services, roads, railways, posts and the like have collapsed, and the so-called People's Courts are merely an outlet for communal hatred and private feuds, a means of liquidating the rivals of the gangs in power. Only wait until you see how these People's Courts are used as a means of doing away with anyone who seems likely to threaten their position. Anyone with a grudge against a member of the community, especially if he hates someone of higher social status, merely charges that poor fellow with counter-revolutionary plotting; and the so-called court does the rest. The wretched chap's property is confiscated or he is hanged. Sometimes both. And all this is taking place over some hundreds of square miles.'

'Now, be fair', remonstrated Rao, who had been trying without success to interrupt our legal friend. 'You know the Government is doing a better job than you imply. It's getting a grip on the situation, even though it doesn't work as rapidly as we would like to see them move. You know that troops and police officers have been drafted in large numbers and that there are a number of towns in which law and order has been restored.'

'Only on the surface has order been restored in those towns. As someone has said: "Government functions during the day and packs up at night." It is a game of hide and seek.'

Rao did not seem to agree, but he could not contradict either. He sat there and pondered.

'Government is merely treating a few of the minor symptoms and is not eradicating the causes of the disease', continued Shahid Ali. 'You've got to feed people, not hand them patriotic window

62

dressing! So long as our Government is foolish enough to refuse to think about people's bellies, I suppose the seeds of Communism will have good opportunity to germinate.'

'You said that the trouble had nothing to do with Communism', I declared.

'Lenin said that out of a hundred so-called Bolsheviks there is one Communist, thirty-nine criminals and sixty fools', he continued. 'Well, you will see these fools ruled by criminals, and I will wager that somewhere in the background lurks the real, Moscow-trained Communist.'

'Of course', said Rao, 'this country is a fine forcing house for Communism. Western countries are protected by their traditions of ordered liberty, their spirit of tolerance and their highly developed social consciousness, but the East possesses no such bulwark against Bolshevism. Here, as in Russia, we have primitive and backward masses, a weak middle class, a tradition of bureaucratic rule and genuine social grievance. That is why Stalin looked to the East. That is why a Russian poet wrote these lines. I saw a translation in a Communist rag:

> Holy Mother Earth is shaken by the tread
> of millions of marching feet. The East has
> lifted its sword. I saw tawny Chinamen
> leering through the windows of the Urals.
> India washes its garments as for a festival.'

The train came to a stop and we were interrupted in our chatter by the ticket collector who was escorted by two policemen. The small wayside station was barbwired and sandbagged as though it were a frontline post.

'The trouble', said Rao when the train moved on, 'is due to lack of education. Our ignorance is colossal, and anything intelligent is suspect. Why? Because there is no general education. There is nothing that the rabble fear more than intelligence. What we need is proper education. . . .'

'I entirely disagree', said Shahid Ali. 'It's folly to assume that more doses of democracy and education will turn the rabble into good citizens. Democracy was never intended for degenerates such as we are today. Our choice is between social chaos and a dictatorship and we are merely inviting turmoil by forcing these muddled notions of democracy on our people.'

'Nonsense!' exclaimed Rao. 'The first step must always be to give to the people the right to vote, then to educate them to use it properly. Adult franchise will give us training in democratic ways and, after that, we must educate our future masters.'

'Democracy is nonsense, Rao Sahib, because it allows the mob to govern our life. By all means consult the masses, but in heaven's name do not be guided by them! As for education, aren't our universities producing an army of graduates for whom there are not enough white-collar jobs? How does that help? These half-educated boys are the most dangerous enemies that ever faced the social order.'

'By education', said Rao, 'I do not mean only academic degrees. I mean teaching the young to think, so that they can see the hollowness of age-old dogma and prejudices.'

'Fine words butter no parsnips', said Shahid Ali. 'This education will turn harmless and reasonably contented primitives into dangerous savages. What kind of education do you want? The whole system is in your hands now, not in the hands of those whom you used to blame for all our ills. You have the power to change and transform. Why not do it?'

Rao left at Hanampur and we continued on our tedious journey. I was feeling somewhat sleepy. Our train halted at a wayside station. All round were fields almost up to the railroad track and, here and there, we could see groups of men and women working. It was a familiar, peaceful scene; no one could associate this normal life of the countryside with violence or disorder. Close to the track I could see a group of villagers sitting and smoking, with their black home-spun blankets thrown over their heads and shoulders to protect them from the sun. Those blankets were their constant attire; they were always there, whether it was hot or cold.

Suddenly, as the train slowly moved off, two men dressed in trousers and bush-shirts ran from behind the field-workers and swung themselves on to our carriage. Quickly they opened the door and pulled themselves up into the compartment which I shared with the lawyer Shahid Ali. Their entry did not strike me as odd, because it was quite common at these wayside stops for people to enter from the side opposite the platform. They seated themselves, studied us intently and chain-smoked while the train picked up speed.

'Where are you going?' the older man asked me abruptly, speaking in Urdu, the official language of the State.

'To Karammett', I replied innocently.

'Why?' he asked, with a scowl.

'Why? I'm just going', I answered.

'Just going!' repeated the man, raising his eyebrows.

'Wait a minute!' interrupted Shahid Ali laying his hand on my knee. 'What is it to do with you? He doesn't have to tell you his business, after all.'

64

'Who says so?' snarled the other, giving Shahid Ali a shove into the corner seat. 'You'll do as we say!'

I could see the bulge of a revolver in his hip-pocket.

The younger man, who had a more refined appearance, asked his companion to take it easy. He spoke in Telugu, the language of the countryside, but with the accent peculiar to the East Coast. The burly older chap subsided and the younger, bending forward a bit in his seat, addressed us. He spoke flawless English, but again with that distinctive accent.

'If you are thinking of pulling the emergency cord', he said with a sardonic smile, 'forget it, because it might have unpleasant results.'

Encouraged by his English, I addressed myself to him.

'Exactly what is it you want? What have you against us?'

'We've got nothing against you so far', he retorted. 'We only want to see the papers of this lawyer friend of yours here. He is planning to argue tomorrow on the wrong side, and we mean to see that he doesn't get the opportunity to perpetuate injustice.'

Suddenly he stood up, snatched the brief case from Shahid Ali's hands, snapped it open, took a swift glance at the papers inside, picked out one or two and tore them up.

'I hope you will know better in future than to try and defend the bastard landlords of this area', he said crisply. He turned to me and after an interminable moment of glaring into my face, said: 'You see, we knew this gentleman was going to Karammett to argue on behalf of a landlord in a lawsuit against the legitimate occupants of land. We didn't hear about you, but I imagine you are a Government official. Well, this is what you and your law are doing. We've hounded out this leech of a landlord from his village and distributed the land to the poor landless peasants. And, sitting in some far off town, you officials and these lawyers work to return the land to that blood-sucker! You are well paid to do it; he by the landlord and you by the Government. Yet some of you officials believe you are impartial? Well, no one is impartial in this struggle. You are either for us or against us.'

'Why should we be for or against anybody?' I ventured. 'After all, the Government is here to protect everybody. Obviously, no government can allow violence to go unchallenged.'

'Yes! Government is for everybody, and your law courts are for justice', he snarled, pointing towards Shahid Ali. 'What justice is there when this man's client alone owns almost all the tillable land in this part of the district—this taluk—while the poor of entire villages are no more than his servants? As for violence, you must be new here, otherwise you would have known who started

65

it all. Do you pretend not to know that Jagga Reddi, the Deshmukh of this area, actually took to hunting men because he got tired of hunting tigers? Yes, sir. We are violent, but only in self-defence.'

I was surprised equally by his eloquence and his vehemence. The other man now warned him that it was time to get off. As the train puffed slowly up slightly rising ground, they opened the carriage door and swung off to the hard roadbed with the agility of cats, an agility obviously born of long practice.

As our train drew up at the next stop, I was relieved to see Shiv Ram waiting on the platform. He was the District Superintendent of Police, who was to be my host for the next two days.

After hurried greetings, I told him of our visitors. Quickly conferring with his men and instructing them to comb the area, he turned to me and asked if the man who had spoken in English had a round scar on his forehead. I nodded. 'Then, sir, you've had the privilege of meeting Comrade Pentaya, the Area Commander, your very first day here.'

'What do you mean by Area Commander?' I asked. 'And how could anyone called Pentaya speak such English?' (Pentaya is a name found exclusively among the poor and illiterate.)

'Pentaya is his party name', Shiv Ram explained. 'His real name, according to our reports, is Ramalinga Reddi. He is the son of a big landlord of the Krishna District of Madras. When he came for "Ug"—which is party parlance for "underground"—he adopted a pseudonym in keeping with the names of the humblest folk of this area. The party members won't let anyone call them Durra, since that is the word applied to landlords here. They insist on the villagers' calling them "anna", elder brother, at most. The day we do the same, this problem will be solved.'

That remark showed Shiv Ram as a new type of police officer still rare in the service.

'It's all something new, you know, and we have not yet shown the imagination this problem requires', he continued, as he drove me to his house in a jeep. 'If these men were mere dacoits, robbing for gain, they could never have survived in the face of the large force of men we have built up here. No, sir! A mere handful of men could not have held us at bay without at least the grudging support of the villagers. We estimate there are only about thirty to forty properly indoctrinated Communists in the area. I have a force under me of nearly a thousand men. Yet what is happening? Their chaps interrogate you in the train itself!'

66

'What, then, do you think is the real crux of the problem here? What makes up the whole pattern?' I asked eagerly.

'Far from simple', he replied as he dodged two buffaloes wandering unconcerned in the middle of the dusty road. 'You have been away a long time, there is much for you to learn. We'll go into the country and see for ourselves. Late this evening we're making a raid. Come along and you'll see what happens.'

That evening we started out in his jeep. With us we had another officer and six men of the Special Armed Police. We might have been setting out on a hunt. As if he guessed my thoughts, Shiv Ram said: 'It looks like shikar, like hunting, doesn't it? In fact, some of us who have been long enough in this fight have begun to look on it as such; we get an inhuman thrill from the business. We have dehumanised ourselves, as it were. Indeed, there are some of our higher-ups, I am afraid, who judge our work by the number of bumpings off in the area. In this region, there must have been at least a hundred bumped off so far and, as I was telling you this morning, almost all the original thirty to forty Communists are still at large, still causing us trouble. They disguise themselves as peasants and we cannot catch them!'

'But then', I protested, 'you are putting down this sort of violence by violence.'

'Well', he said, 'life is not very sacred in this game. Here in the villages so many die of so many natural causes that a few deaths from this man-made cause make little difference to them. But what does not go down with them is meaningless terrorism. The villagers feel it is fair to kill those who attack them. After all, if someone is endangering your life, you have a right, even if it is not a moral right, to kill him first.

'But sometimes we cannot help killing indiscriminately. That the villagers cannot understand. What they do know is that progress is judged by figures, figures of bumping off. Catch a blood-thirsty Communist and kill him and the villagers will have a healthy respect for you. But catch just anybody and kill him, and they not only bitterly resent it, they despise you for your lack of understanding. The objective of the Communist is not to give battle; it is to bring down upon the community in general a reprisal for his wrongs, in the hope that fury and resentment roused by punishment meted out to the innocent will certainly swell the ranks of those from whom they will draw new recruits and build up opposition to authority. That's where the hitch is, and that is where trouble starts.'

We were travelling along a winding road with bush-covered

hillocks on either side. Shiv Ram gave an order for the men to release the safety-catches of their rifles. After covering a good distance through the jungle we reached the village for which we were heading at last. A man had been killed there the day before for cultivating a landlord's field on the authority of the Government Revenue Court which, by decision of the self-appointed Communist People's Court, should have been tilled by another. The tiller was therefore eliminated by murder.

As we entered the village not a soul was in sight. The village looked bleak and deserted; a scummy sterility hung over it. This was a strange experience for me, for in the old days the first villagers to see an official vehicle would flock around it, some from a sense of duty, some to pursue grievances and some out of curiosity. Today nobody greeted us. Yet this was evening, when all the villagers would normally be at home. A few old women and children peeped through the doorways of their thatched huts, perhaps waiting to approach us if assured of the benevolence of our mood.

'Go and get the bastards!' shouted Shiv Ram. We sat under the banyan tree and waited. I could still see the marks of blood where the man must have been slaughtered. The Communists had cut his throat at that traditional gathering spot of the village, and the whole village must have witnessed the ghastly incident.

As we were waiting, Shiv Ram gave me a brief outline of the organisation of the Communists. The entire region was under the direction of a committee of the party and an Area Commander; the latter was the younger of the two men I had encountered in the train. The area was sub-divided into various zones. The smallest organised group was called a 'dallam' or platoon, consisting of some three or four men; one dallam leader and one political agent in the zone usually had sten guns. The armed men who formed the militant section were mostly men from these very villages, men with a grievance, raw recruits who also came from the area but were given only sticks and muzzle-loaders.

To provide a man with a rifle was to recognise formally that he had proved himself worthy of full-fledged membership of the party. The orders were that, next to the life of the dallam leader, the rifle was to be preserved at all cost. There were cases where men even ran naked, shedding clothes which might get caught in jungle bushes, but never once letting go of their rifles.

The political agent was almost always from the south; it was his duty to educate the dallam politically. He did next to no military planning and was concerned only with the indoctrination of the group.

The area headquarters was at some undiscovered and ever-shifting spot in the jungle. There, the Communists had duplicating machines and an office from which they circulated instructions and party papers. Communist magazines, books and simple medical stores (for in that area there was no governmental medical aid available) were supplied to them from the city, presumably by the innumerable poor, unemployed and disillusioned intellectuals, who wanted nothing better than to spite the Government which they blamed for preserving the dead weight of privilege and the misery around them.

'The aim of all this organisation, don't forget, is to spread suspicion, upset law and order and disrupt the even tenor of their lives. This they do by terrorism, the horror of deliberate murder, of ambush or a crude bomb.'

I could see that while Shiv Ram was a bitter and convinced anti-Communist he was not satisfied with the way his seniors were running the show. He was perplexed by their lack of imagination and of genuine insight into the people's problems. He criticised well-meaning administrators; it was often the good administrator, he said, who found it difficult to change a bad system. He could never forget that the present state of affairs was brought about largely by the cruel exploitation of the villagers by the Deshmukhs and the corruption that prevailed in this area. Those who had been a meek and affable people were now in bloody revolt. And what they were offered was only law and order, accompanied by the reinstatement of the same Deshmukhs to the seat of power. At this rate, the struggle would never end. The Government must come out on the side of the people and announce that, while they would restore law and order, they would not restore exploitation.

As the men were slowly brought in, I saw in their faces only suspicion and fear.

'There are either neutral villages or hostile villages, but no friendly ones as yet. And unless we can get friendly villages we cannot solve this problem', said Shiv Ram, as he looked at the men and began a prolonged interrogation. Every one of them denied having seen the killing at all, although it was certain that it must have been a public occurrence. Everyone professed ignorance and said that gutta durralu* had done it, and that by their very coming the villagers had been so frightened that they had run away. They would not budge from this explanation and at last Shiv Ram lost his temper.

'Take them to headquarters', he said in a commanding tone.

* 'Hill masters', so called because the hills were the Communist stronghold.

'Two days in the open pens there and the bastards will speak! Take every able-bodied male away, and for the rest we will levy a collective fine on the village which will teach them a lesson!'

'But, Durra', protested a sad-eyed old woman who had moved closer to us, 'this is the harvesting season; what will I do without my son, Ashigadu?' And to fortify her pathetic appeal she raised a shaking, withered hand towards her two little grandchildren who stood in the opening of the hut with their match-stick legs and protruding bellies. 'These motherless children will be all that I shall be left with.' The words came muffled from a toothless mouth.

'Tell your gutta durralu that', Shiv Ram shouted. 'If you had not allowed them to kill a man this would not have happened.'

'Come, let's go', he said, 'that's all we can get here or in any village these days. It's sickening, but it can't be helped.'

And as we got into the jeep he turned to me and, pointing to the nearby hills, said: 'I am sure those bastards are in those hills this very moment, watching us. I must have that area combed, and I am sure as soon as our backs are turned one of the villagers will go and report all this to them. Of course, the villagers must have given them advance information of our arrival by shouting or imitating some particular bird or animal call. And if they know you too were with me at this drama you may become a marked man, you know.'

With that reflection we returned home.

Shiv Ram and I spent the whole of the next day looking through his reports, diaries and the memoranda which the Government had prepared on the situation. I saw original documents seized in police raids which contained outlines of techniques for guerilla warfare, appeals to 'dear children', to 'student comrades', to 'heroic mothers' and to police and army personnel. Almost all of these documents advocated extreme forms of violence and exhorted people to 'keep up the hatred'. 'Kill the enemy by the use of incendiaries, by mixing poison in the food, learn the technique of destruction.' A circular advised: 'Throw grenades through windows and over the walls and, if opportunity presents, set fire to the house.... You will move disguised as ryots (peasants) during evenings and nights, after carefully examining the movements of the enemy, and throw grenades....' A pamphlet in the local language appealed to 'heroic mothers' to 'cut their enemy's throats and drink their blood'. Other documents laid down various brutal methods to destroy adversaries.

The Communists had done their best to create famine conditions in the area. Shiv Ram showed me how they had burnt

70

houses and rice ricks worth thirty thousand rupees, how they had set fire to maize stores in Nagireddigudam. They were destroying bridges and burning chowdis. In the information collected I found the following note: 'More than five hundred armed Communists raided the village of Peddavid . . . murdered ten villagers, including women and children, and severely injured the others. Children were thrown into the fire. Seventy houses had been set on fire; all gutted. In the blaze, two women were burnt to death. This incident was a reprisal, as one of the villagers of Peddavid had informed the police of the presence in the neighbourhood of Kot Karain, a notorious Communist outlaw. A number of Communists made a surprise attack on the village of Dundrampalli. . . . They first overpowered and shot dead six villagers who had been keeping watch. Then they attacked the inmates of twelve houses. Six of the villagers were seized, taken outside the village and brutally done to death with sten gun and rifle fire. Sixteen people, including a woman, were kidnapped by Communists at a place near Pengot and were taken to Lingagiri. The men were murdered and their bodies set on fire. The charred bodies were later found lying near Lingagiri border. There was no trace of the woman. . . .'

We waded for hours through this seemingly incredible and sickening catalogue of crimes and atrocities, for which chapter and verse were quoted. I was shocked and stunned. But perhaps it is only in conditions of utter misery and widespread discontent that the promises of a paradise would appear to carry any value.

6 Fruits of Despair

NEXT morning I had to go to an old college friend of mine, Ranga Rao, who lived some distance away in the security of a big town, Nadira, guarded by a large police force. Shiv Ram drove me there in his jeep. Ranga Rao had lived for years in his own village, but had lately moved to this well-guarded town for safety, and to educate his children. Though a big land-owner and a Patwari, he was one of those educated men who actively, sometimes openly, had helped the nationalist cause and suffered in one way or another under the old regime. He had even gone to prison for a few days. He was not unpopular in the countryside, though there were many who could not reconcile his calling with his nationalism.

He had a somewhat troubled home life, principally because of disagreements with his elderly father, who had remarried after the death of his mother. I used to visit Ranga Rao's house during the long summer holidays, but after I entered the service of the State we lost touch with one another for some time. Then, later, I was posted to the same area where Ranga Rao and his family lived.

I remember how he had explained the complicated village accounting system to me and had taken the trouble to coach me in the intricacies of the village officer's network of petty graft. I remember too how vexed he was when I jailed his own Gumashta (agent), the first victim of my new-found knowledge! I knew his two sons, who were said to be doing well at school, and his small, pretty daughter. Ranga Rao had again invited me to be his guest and I readily accepted his invitation, for I was sure that besides renewing our old friendship, something to which I had looked forward during the past few years, I should pick up some first hand knowledge of the happenings in the locality.

Ranga Rao's father had died a year before; his wife and children were away staying in the city as schools were closed for the summer holidays. His house, built in the old-fashioned way, was completely at our disposal. That day we talked mostly about his family affairs, the trouble he had to face and the ugly situation that had developed. The night was hot; our cots were set on the roof of the house. There, under the sky, we talked till late about all that had happened in the District. Ranga Rao told me strange stories of espionage and counter-espionage carried on day and night by the frustrated officers of a nervous Government; of bribery, collusion and other evil doings. There was only one interruption in our talks: a little after midnight I heard someone creeping along the wall.

'It is all right', Ranga Rao said quietly as he heard light taps on the rocks. It was Khasim, the watchman; the taps were his prearranged signal that all was well at the front gate. We continued our conversation.

Ranga Rao went on relating horrible tales of atrocities. A goods train had recently been stopped and an innocent railway officer shot dead by the Communists. A police party was ambushed and slaughtered in cold blood. He told me that a once prosperous community would get nothing now from anyone but a tear. Ranga Rao's own view was that there was not much doctrinaire Communism, as such, in the area and very little understanding of Communist principles.

'Can you blame these simple folk for following such methods when the Communists promise them everything?' he asked. 'Hard-pressed as he is, what the villager wants today is food, clothing and shelter', he continued. 'He does not care for the freedom which the Government talks about. The tragedy of it all is that rogues have taken advantage of the situation to gain their own ends. Anyone with a grudge can pay off old scores by pretending to be a Communist.'

Here are a few stories typical of those he told me that night.

Rajigah was an active member of the Depressed Classes Association. He had been struggling for some months to collect data about the social and economic disabilities of his community so that he could represent their grievances to the Tehsildar. One fine morning he was served with a warrant for the alleged theft of a buffalo. Those who knew him intimately were willing to declare on oath that his previous record was untainted, that he was above suspicion. Rajigah was bewildered at the accusation. Later developments showed that the village Patwari had

73

schemed to clap him in jail because his activities were proving uncomfortable to his authority.

Rajigah owned a small plot of dry land, encompassed by some trees. The Patwari had a petition written by the village Bania on behalf of an old widow, complaining that her buffalo had been stolen. Her thumb impression was obtained, as a substitute for a signature, by telling her that it was an application for a tac-cavi loan. Her buffalo was tied to one of the trees on Rajigah's land. A punchnama was held and a warrant of arrest obtained. But the old widow deposed that it was the Patwari who had taken out the buffalo for grazing, that it was never stolen. The case was dismissed.

But this was not Rajigah's first experience of the treatment which awaits a social worker. Once he had been waylaid by unknown miscreants. On another occasion his jawar harvest, his only means of subsistence, had been stolen by thieves from a neighbouring village. If the poor members of his community had not helped him with money scrimped and saved from their meagre and uncertain wages, he would have starved for the whole season. Rajigah was an honest man; he treated these donations as loans and returned them when better days dawned on him.

This charge of theft, however, was too much for him. He planned to give up his public work in sheer disgust. But certain 'idealists' in a nearby village, calling themselves Communists, knowing his worth as an indefatigable and conscientious man, persuaded him to join their dallam. They guaranteed him complete immunity from the petty harassment which had so far been his lot. 'Work for a wider cause and help your own men into the bargain. We observe no caste or communal distinctions. And we'll see who can harass you in future', they said.

Rajigah succumbed to the temptation. Another solid citizen had joined the ranks of the declared enemies of law and order.

Lingiah had borrowed fifty rupees from the village Bania on the occasion of his daughter's marriage and had promised to return the amount by the next harvest. Lingiah's next crop was good; he would be able to pay his debt. But the Bania was anxious that the debt should not be repaid the same year. He would lose interest. Covertly, he instigated litigation against Lingiah. A certain Ramanujam was jealous of Lingiah, partly because his land was more fertile, but mainly because the girl whom Ramanujam had wanted to marry had become Lingiah's wife. The Bania knew that Ramanujam would agree to bring a suit, and he did.

74

Lingiah was shocked at the news but felt certain that Ramanujam had no case against him. Since the matter had gone to court, though, he had to do something to counteract the sinister move. He approached the Bania and told him that he would not be able to repay the loan, as he had been unnecessarily dragged to the court.

'Don't worry', said the Bania, 'this is not a matter of life and death for you. You may repay the loan whenever you can, but fight out this case we must. If you need any more money, you can rely upon me.'

Lingiah thanked him and busied himself with the litigation, which lingered on for months before it was dismissed. Lingiah was out of pocket to the amount of another seventy-five rupees and now owed the Bania a hundred and twenty-five rupees plus compound interest at the rate of four per cent per mensem.

The next crop was not a good one. Prices of foodgrains also had fallen. What Lingiah earned could hardly meet his seed and food requirements. Again he excused himself from the payment of his loan. The Bania filed a suit against him for the recovery of the loan and interest. This, however was not all. His little hut was set on fire while he was busy in his field and his meagre belongings were reduced to ashes. Lingiah was faced with the problem of repaying the loan and replacing his hut with its accessories. He was sitting under a tree with his wife and his little child, brooding over his fate, when the Bania approached him with sighs and tears.

'My sympathies are with you my friend', he said. 'I shall withdraw my suit against you and make a small advance of another hundred rupees. All you have to do is to mortgage your land with me as security for the loan.'

Lingiah was reluctant. The Bania spoke to his wife in a tone of sympathy mixed with persuasion. The woman agreed and so did Lingiah. The land was mortgaged for two hundred and fifty rupees. But Lingiah's fate never improved. At the end of two years his land, which was worth over a thousand, was auctioned for three hundred rupees in the name of the village Bania. Lingiah and his wife are now leading nomadic lives as leaders of a Communist dallam.

Now take this typical village scene. The villagers have all gathered under a banyan tree to listen to the Tehsildar, who is scheduled to speak about his grain procurement campaign. White-clad local volunteers, home guards or whatever they were called, are seen moving about, arranging chairs and benches and appeal-

75

ing to the people there to remain quiet and disciplined. Then the audience is told that it should applaud loudly when the leader claps his hands.

The Tehsildar, accompanied by his levy procurement staff and the local leaders, arrives at about five o'clock. Buttermilk is served. Local political workers are introduced to the Tehsildar, who then addresses the gathering: 'Friends, you are aware that, for reasons beyond our control, India is producing much less food than she needs. Floods, cyclones, pests, drought and other calamities have wrought untold havoc. Our dollar and sterling reserves are being depleted due to huge imports of foodgrains from other countries. We can minimise this drain on our wealth by maximum procurement and equitable distribution of food-grains. You have been lucky that your village has been spared these ravages. I, therefore, ask you to sell to the Government your entire surplus so that non-cultivators may be fed from Government stores.'

The local Congress leader, ostensibly supporting the Tehsildar's appeal, asks the villagers to tell the Tehsildar Sahib whatever they have to say in the matter.

A fat, pot-bellied gentleman stands up and says that the crop has failed in the village. The produce is not even half that of the previous year. Prices of cloth, iron and steel have gone up. The village grain bank is claiming a share of their produce for the common pool, in the name of the co-operative movement; there-fore, if any grain is taken out of the village it will mean misery and starvation for the villagers. The entire gathering applauds these remarks.

He is followed by two other speakers, more vehement in tone, who appeal to the Tehsildar Sahib to open a cheap grain shop in the village and to send some grain to the shop from the Taluk Headquarters and to arrange for feeding the poor at least twice a week. When the gathering lustily cheers the demands, the Tehsildar holds quiet consultation with a few of the local leaders and also with the Patel and the Patwari. Ultimately he decides that no grain would be procured from the village, provided the rich agree to look after the poor of the village. Cries of 'Mahatma Gandhi Ki Jai' rend the air, and he is seen off by the whole crowd which walks behind his cart for more than a mile.

When the gathering reassembles under the same banyan tree after getting rid of the Tehsildar, the leaders congratulate each other and the gathering for having averted a catastrophe. Twelve hundred maunds of rice and two thousand maunds of jawar from that village are sold on the black market that season. The poor, of course, have to remain content with one meal a day. The Communist Party enrolls thirty members from the village for its fighting squad.

Most Indian villages do not know what sanitation means. Kusuma-palli was no exception. Here were heaps of cow-dung soon to be turned into fuel, stinking drains with flies and mosquitoes hovering about them. Dozens of unwashed buffaloes grazing near-by. Untidy children, bare-headed and bare-footed, with their hands soaked in mud, pelted stones at the nearest fruit tree, picked up their booty with their soiled hands and swallowed it. An old woman groaning with pain lay half-naked in an airless hovel. In a corner of the hut was tied up an ailing cow, while the veranda of the dwelling was used as kitchen-cum-dining-room. When the wind blows it deposits the village dirt on this veranda. There were more deaths than births in this village last year, and there was not a house here without an eczema patient. The village quack had been doing such a roaring trade that he could maintain about a dozen buffaloes and cows, and store in one of his underground cells enough rice and wheat to keep the entire village alive for more than a month. His kitchen garden below the village well produced vegetables and bananas which he sold at high prices to the villagers and passers-by. The villagers, of course, made their purchases on credit, while others paid cash. When the debt exceeded ten rupees the quack demanded that the debtor should allow him to milk his buffalo, free of charge, until the debt was liquidated. The other prosperous inhabitants of the village, owning brick houses, kitchen gardens and fertile lands, were the Patel, the Patwari, the Bania and the Pujari (priest). The Deshmukh had a bungalow which he rarely used, except for storing paddy, wheat and fodder.

Ramsingh of Kusumapalli, who had returned from the District town after passing his matriculation examination, felt that all was not well with his village. He asked the elders for their help in his proposed campaign of sanitation, hygiene and rural recon-struction. All of them nodded assent.

That very evening, the Patwari held a meeting of all the im-portant men in the village in the Deshmukh's deserted bungalow. Taking them into his confidence, he said in low tones: 'Ram-singh seems to have lost his head. We have so far been immune from official vigilance and public gaze, firstly because our village has not been chosen as a rural reconstruction centre, and secondly because it is not easily accessible from the main road. We have, in fact, enjoyed complete village autonomy. If Ramsingh's scheme succeeds, the Agricultural Department, the Co-operative Department, the Veterinary Department, the Department of Education—in fact, every Department—will try to poke their noses into our business and bother us.'

'Even the Public Health Department will start injecting poison and ruin the health of the villagers', interrupted the quack.

'And then the Agricultural Department will come in with supplies of seeds and manure and with their indiscriminate loans', sighed the Bania.

'Wailing and sighing will not do. We must do something to prevent this mischief', thundered the Patwari.

'Why worry? Ramsingh is here only for the vacation. He was telling me that he would return to the city for higher education', said the old priest, consoling the rest.

'Two months is long enough a period for this mischief to gain momentum and encircle all of us', warned the Patel, and added: 'I know how to get rid of him. I shall report to the Sub-Inspector of Police that Ramsingh is preaching Communism in the village and say that if he is not checked immediately life and property in the village will be endangered.'

'But a mere report will not do. To impress upon the authorities that we are really afraid of Ramsingh's activities, we should place in the hands of the Sub-Inspector two hundred rupees, a round sum, for such use as he thinks fit', one declared.

'That might weaken our case. He may think that we are trying to bribe him to do something which he need not have done', said another.

'I don't think so. If we back up our report by presenting a small purse it would only show how nervous we have grown as a result of Ramsingh's activities. Also, that we are willing to sacrifice a round sum of two hundred rupees to regain our lost sense of security', advised a third.

This was agreed to. Two hundred rupees were collected there and then and paid to the Sub-Inspector. On the fourth day, newspaper vendors in towns and cities were heard shouting: 'Prominent Communist Arrested'; 'Villagers Hand Over Red Leader to the Police'; 'Mysterious Ramsingh Captured At Last'.

Next came another story. A young civil servant named Pershad, aged twenty-seven, duly trained in revenue administration, was posted as a Deputy Collector in a District. A graduate in economics, with a degree in law, an ex-president of the College Union, he had come first in the competitive examination and was known for the integrity of his character and the clarity of

78

his views. His training in the Civil Service under a British officer held in high esteem by the public, had added grace and charm to the young officer's versatility. Before he ventured out to his District headquarters his friends and relatives honoured him with a farewell party. Replying to the speeches on the occasion he assured the gathering that he would never compromise his integrity and the cause of truth and justice at any cost.

A few months after assuming charge of his Division he was directed by the Collector to proceed on a tour of inspection. Equipped with files and law books, Pershad set out on his mission. He took care to see that he had a good stock of everything required for the kitchen, as he never believed in accepting local invitations while on tour. In fact, he had been warned against this pernicious system. He carried his own camp cot, a small tent, a hurricane lantern and other requisites. Wherever he went, he camped, he studied the place and its requirements, settled disputes on the spot and removed any inequities of revenue assessments. He had finished hardly half a dozen villages, when stories about his being a strict official, unamenable to the advice of Patels and Patwaris, started spreading through the area. When a poor peasant complained to him that an amount of one hundred rupees borrowed by him from the Bania had swollen within six months to two hundred and fifty, Pershad, taking upon himself the duties of a Debt Conciliation Officer, had scrutinised the account books of the Bania, taken local evidence and had managed to reduce the debt to one hundred and six rupees. Many such stories reached the inhabitants of Bakkalguda, one of the villages where Pershad was due to arrive.

The Patwari, the Patel, the Pujari, the Bania and a few of the big landowners met in secret conference to consider the situation arising from the 'Communist' tendencies of the new Deputy Collector.

'They say that he has ordered Keshulu to give up the possession of his lands in favour of Aslam Khan, who had put in a petition that the lands belonged to him but had been forcibly taken by Keshulu and his brothers', said the Patwari. He added: 'This would embolden Shaik Chand and Mohammed Ibrahim of our village to make similar claims against us. Where will we be if the Deputy Collector goes on sanctioning all such applications?'

'I hear that the Patwari of Jamikunta had reported that Satyanarayana was too poor to pay his arrears of land revenue, but the Deputy Collector, after local investigation, not merely collected the arrears on the spot but also obtained a donation from him for flood relief funds', whispered the Patel.

79

'That is too bad', said the Pujari. 'You can't compel a man to give donations. Let us send a letter to the local paper.'

'It will be indiscreet to write a letter to the local paper against the Deputy Collector. He collected the donations in the presence of the entire village, and I hear that Satyanarayana volunteered this amount to save himself from penalties and even prosecution. The Deputy Collector had ample evidence of Satyanarayana's hoarded grain and black market activities.'

'The question now is what we should do to keep this menace away from our doors', the Patwari added.

Confabulations continued behind closed doors. Nothing is known of what transpired. However, the tragic sequel appeared in the city newspapers four days later: 'Mr Pershad, a popular Revenue Officer, was waylaid by an armed gang of masked Communists on his way to Bakkalguda on the night of October 14 and has not been seen since. Investigations are in progress.'

By this time it was nearly three o'clock in the morning, but Ranga Rao and I continued our talk.

'My own villages, as you know, are in the irrigated zone and are not so badly off, owing to the high price of grain', he said. 'But costs have risen too, and there is little manure, no iron for plough-shares, no kerosene oil. We object to the grain price fixed by Government. However the agitators have not been able to make much headway in this area. Even a little prosperity can keep the devil at a distance.'

'Where are we going the day after tomorrow?' I asked. 'I want to go to Venkatapur first.'

'Yes, I knew you couldn't miss Venkatapur. We'll go there but I would like also to take you to the non-irrigated area dominated by the Communists.'

'Do any officials visit these villages?'

'Occasionally, to qualify for their travelling allowances. They seldom see places off the motor road. A saloon car is so much more comfortable than a bullock-cart or a horse, and the police escort can follow one's big car by lorry. That is how they study the situation. Only the other day our Deputy Inspector General of Police drove out a full eighty miles—in the hot weather, too—stayed half an hour in a headquarters village and then drove the eighty miles back to report that all these rumours of a Communist rebellion were sheer nonsense. He hadn't even seen any Reds!'

It was getting late and I retired to bed but not to sleep. I tried to write my daily diary in bed with the aid of an electric torch, but I gave up the effort. Then I slipped out of the mosquito net and walked to the terrace.

It all seemed so peaceful, as peaceful as it was quiet, as I stood there and contemplated the faint outline of the town I had known. No indication of trouble here, I thought, as I looked out over the housetops, down the streets. This community had not been an Eden, but it had been a pleasant place to live in, especially for a District Officer. The executive conferences, the round-table meetings on District problems, the bridge parties, the tennis matches: what an interesting life it had been! Where were they all? Where was Narayan Reddi and Abdur Rahman and Naki and Sitaram Rao and O'Neill, the Burma-Shell agent? Ranga Rao had not mentioned a single one of them. They had all been his close friends. In fact, as I thought over our conversation of that night, I could not recall his mentioning any one of our old friends. That kind of behaviour from a man who loved his friends and enjoyed their companionship in the rich, full-blooded way bespoke true friendship!

I slumped down in the wicker chair, and sat still, listened and thought, as the waning moon and the myriads of stars painted a scene of beauty which is to be found only in India about an hour or so before dawn.

I fell asleep in that chair and had to be awakened by Ranga Rao. I was embarrassed, for fear he might think I had been afraid to relax for the night.

'You were always an oddity', he commented, as we began our breakfast of paratas, fried eggs and tea. 'Always, always, a strange character', he added with a smile.

'Many a time I have heard you say that you never cared for normal people', I replied.

'That probably explains my great affection for you', he commented.

We went out to roam the town. It was good to move here and there, to be greeted by old friends, to be met by people who reminded me how much I had helped them with their problems of land or grain when I was there previously. No one accosted us; no one bothered us in any way. Walking back to Ranga Rao's house, I commented on the peaceful life of the community in spite of the barbed wire.

'Yet', Ranga Rao said, shaking his head, 'they were there around you all the time.'

He stopped as though to think more clearly. 'Remember the man in the black shepherd's cape who stood over near the wall? Recall the beggar near the Chowdi?'

G

I nodded, for I had seen both.

'That beggar, with his shortened leg, is one of the best rifle shots in the District ... and there are others', he declared.

I stayed with Ranga Rao for another day before we went into the countryside. I wanted to attend the Magistrate's Court to witness the trial of Aggi Reddi, a Communist leader who was being charged with murder. The hearing of the case was adjourned for that day because an important witness could not be produced. This turn of affairs gave me an opportunity to talk to Comrade Aggi Reddi, thanks to Shiv Ram, who had instructed his Inspector to arrange the interview.

Aggi Reddi was handcuffed and fettered, a young man, perhaps in his late twenties: tall and brown, with thick lips and a furtive manner. His bearing was nervous, self-conscious, as though he were hiding some deep irritation. He was dressed in a roughly-woven shirt and a cloth fastened round his loins; he was an 'under trial' and the prison authorities had not yet supplied him with the ochre-coloured pants and shirt prescribed for the convicted. As he entered the room, he did not look me in the face and I saw that he was suspicious. He appeared a little surprised when I offered him a chair but, after introducing myself, I said that I wanted to speak to him in confidence. At first he did not seem to believe me, but as I spoke of the work I was doing he relaxed a little and his attitude softened.

'Let me assure you', I said, 'that I am not trying to get any information out of you. That, others will do perhaps, but I am not interested in it. I just want to understand you. I am aware of the problems you want to solve, but I am interested today in the problems that must have created you.'

'That's the trouble with you and your lot. I have heard of your work', he said, replying, to my surprise, in a cool collected manner but with a touch of obvious contempt. 'You try to find an answer for everything in the mind of man, anywhere, in fact, except in the real place, in your society based on exploitation. No, I am afraid you won't find in me the answer to any problem except the problems that we have set out to solve ourselves.'

I sensed that I had made a wrong beginning and so, to change the approach, I asked bluntly: 'All right, let me put it this way. Have all these murders really been committed? Have you, who sit and talk on such a high level, killed people with your own hands?'

'I was only on the political side', he said in a deliberate tone, 'but I do not want to shirk my responsibility. I led dallams that

82

killed men. I ordered the killing and I was a witness to some of them. I killed a few in self-defence, of course.'

As he sat there, what struck me most about him were his penetrating eyes. There was a transparent radiance about them, a fierceness which somehow reminded me of the philosopher and mystic Aurobindo, whom I had met years ago in Pondicherry. I remember coming out of Aurobindo's room unable to see anything but his eyes. So, also, as I looked at this young man, I felt that I would remember his eyes too for a long time.

Suddenly aware of the silence that hung in the air, I started out of a momentary trance brought on both by the young man's hypnotic gaze and by the somnolent effect of the weather. Hastily I pursued my line of questioning.

'What better world have you created here?' I asked. 'Even from your own point of view, what have you achieved? The people are terrorised, their peaceful life is shattered; they are burdened with additional taxes and this police force prowls about making life difficult for everybody, and all because of your wanting your kind of a better world. How does this make you happy?'

He did not reply at once. He was now on the defensive, but I could see he was touched; his eyes seemed to reflect a kind of tenderness.

'Yes, you are right. The people are suffering. But what can be done? This is the price that has to be paid. And after all, who suffers most? Our people, the labourers and the workers, the landless and the disinherited always suffer; to them this is no new experience. It is your people, the rich, who suffer now for the first time. I don't deny the poor also are suffering, but it is not we who are the cause of it. If we had not engaged in this protest you would have gone on exploiting them as you have been doing for years, but we have driven the Deshmukhs away. You cannot eject the people from the land they now occupy. They also know that; and that is why they support us in spite of all these troubles.'

He was obviously referring to the innumerable illegal occupations of landowners' estates by tenants and landless peasants. There was enough cruel truth behind what he had said to make me feel ill at ease. But I knew that if we continued this line of talk I should only be listening to a political harangue. I wanted to understand the man, not be an audience for him. I arranged for his handcuffs to be removed and for him to be left with me a little longer. I was disturbed mostly by the ideological level from which he was speaking and at the information he had at his command. I had met many public men in Asia, but no ordinary

83

political worker would have had such a firm grasp of his theory and his facts.

At one stage, I remember, Aggi Reddi turned to me and said: 'You know, this little table stands like a barrier between you and me: one that runs all the way round the world. It runs by way of Vietnam to the Yalu river, to the Danube. Everywhere there are men on two sides: one standing for exploitation, feudalism, imperialism, colonialism and the theory of the survival of the fittest; while on the other side is the camp of peace, progress and the rule of "to each according to his need". And you ask me whether I've killed a few men? The new cannot arise without the death of the old. You are decaying, nobody need kill you. This table of separation runs not only round the world, it also runs right through families. If you have young men in your own family you will find them on my side of the table.'

It was getting near lunch time and I offered him a drink and a smoke, which he eagerly accepted. He appeared to relax and became more mellow and more personal. He was the son of a petty clerk who was wrongfully dismissed, he told me. He had left his family after a quarrel and it was during that period when he was studying on his own in the city that he had become a party member. Since then he had lived only on the party allowance.

In the course of his party work he had met Rukki, a young girl student, also a member, and had fallen in love with her. It was, he insisted, as respectable a love affair as any middle class alliance. He quite angrily denied the common slander about free love in the party. It was more difficult, he said, to get the party's agreement to the marriage of two party members than it was to get a father's blessing for a marriage arranged otherwise than under a contract made by the parents, as is the custom in that part of the world. It was only years later, in the forests where both of them were working underground, that he had married Rukki, the girl of his choice.

'You talked of the suffering of the people, Mr Rihaz. Have you ever imagined what some of us have suffered? I spent only the wedding night with my wife and since then I saw her only today in Court. I used to receive her letters, letters which I treasured even though I am a heartless Communist to you; and when the police caught me, they confiscated those letters for no reason at all. Yes, feelings and emotions we too have. Only we feel the more, we want everyone to be able to feel both joy and sorrow. Not as it is now, when some feel joy all the time, while others must always be sorrowful. Swami Vivekananda said: "Every dog must have his day and so must the under-dog".'

84

He was obviously moved when he referred to his wife. He was speaking now of his own accord, in a series of gentle hesitations, steps and starts. He would think for a while with a distant look in his eyes and then burst forth: 'But why do you make such a fuss about the lives of a few hundred people when we are fighting for a great cause? You did not say anything when the atom bombs of the bloodthirsty warmongers brought death, suffering and untold misery to thousands of innocent men, women and children in Hiroshima, when millions of houses were destroyed in air-raids, when thousands of starving people, who were only asserting their right to stop exploitation of themselves, were being brutally liquidated by the imperialists in cold blood in Asia and Africa. Yet if we kill a few parasitic bastards you ask why?'

He paused for a while. 'After all, these lives are abstractions, aren't they? These are the inevitable sacrifices demanded by the cause. It is weakness to think about the victims; think of the goal.'

I could see he knew his Marx well. I encouraged him to continue.

'Our victims are only the casualties of a cause, while your system victimises human beings on a mass scale. What else are the millions of unemployed in peacetime, the millions killed in holding colonial empires and the trade routes of the world? Your system is based on victimisation, ours does away with exploitation. We only want to create a better world for all.'

'But don't you think we also seek the happiness of the people and wouldn't you join us in our peaceful campaign if you are let out?'

'I don't very much care whether I am let out or not. Do you want me to speak frankly?'

'Yes, certainly.'

'I know, Mr Rihaz, that you work among the poor and perhaps sincerely wish their lot to be bettered, but we consider you the real enemy of the people for you want to perpetuate a pernicious system by making people contented with capitalist society, which is the root cause of all evils and which cannot provide any alternative to exploitation, wars and the destruction of the world's human and material resources. You seem to bother about temporary inconveniences, and inconveniences only to yourselves, the well-fed.' He smiled cynically and continued: 'The people are inconvenienced day and night anyway, so they are not bothered about it.'

Aggi Reddi had gained confidence and was speaking with all the fierceness and fanaticism of his creed.

Then he suddenly appeared to quieten down. He thought for a while. 'No, we are no beasts, Mr Rihaz. We are only trying to build a better world. All this suffering is caused by your people standing in the way, not by us.'

I talked to him about measures of social security, of super-taxes and the strength of trade unions in the so-called capitalistic countries. But he interrupted: 'You cannot stand right outside your economic system. You have got to change the system, or you change nothing.'

I realised that the wall of his fanaticism could not be pierced. It was getting late, and the prison authorities had to take him away. When we parted, I somehow felt we had at least understood each other a little. I stepped out of the room. Within view and earshot, Rukki, his wife, was addressing in her native tongue a small crowd which had gathered in the village square: 'We want peace, bread and decent living conditions today. Give us justice or give us death. . . .'

7 Communism and Anarchy

THE next morning we set out for Venkatapur. We did the
first twelve miles in a bus and then another ten miles in a
bullock-cart, over country I had once known so well. Some
years ago Venkatapur had been a quiet village of some seven
hundred inhabitants, isolated until I had made a road joining it
to the main highway. Now my fine road was in a shocking
state. The bullock-cart, never a comfortable vehicle, became an
instrument of torture as it bounced and jolted over pot-holes. I
had difficulty in recognising the last strip of the road which
the proud villagers had constructed by themselves. As I jolted
along, I wondered how long it would really be before the bullock
cart is replaced in our country. Very long, indeed; for it can never
be replaced until we ourselves make enough jeeps and enough
roads and both of these are very distant goals. In a backward
country the indices of progress are often strange. In our country,
for instance, I should say that the progressive elimination of the
bullock-cart might form a good criterion; or, for that matter, even
the replacement of its iron rim by a rubber tyre, for most of
this discomfort was due to the wheel. But then did we have
enough rubber? And that again is a distant goal. So whichever
way I turned, I found how distant and difficult real progress is
in my country.

As we entered the village all was silent at first, save for the
creaking wheels of our own cart. We got down and began walking. I went to the nearest hut. It was the hut of Soniya, the hard-
working farmer whose four children, I remembered, had possessed
the brightest eyes and the happiest expressions I had seen in the
village. As the door was slammed against me, I talked through
the door, as it were, to the inmates. I told them who I was. I
asked Soniya to come out. Finally the door opened and there

87

stood an emaciated and hardly recognisable Soniya. He walked into the street and stood in front of me for several seconds and glared at me with two of the coldest gimlet eyes I ever saw. I speculated about what he would say. I thought of the times he came to me for help, of the loans he was unable to pay to the Bania and of his little children.

He suddenly bowed and touched my feet, and with folded hands almost whispered: 'The village has changed.'

'That's what I've been told', I replied. 'What is the trouble?'

'Durra', he said in a tragic slurring voice, 'we are afraid.'

I could never forget that moment. In that simple sentence Soniya told me the whole story of the tribulation of his people.

'Of what?' I asked.

'You know', was the laconic comment.

I asked him to come along with me to the house of old Pulliah, the rich Bania, whom I had converted to village uplift work.

'Pulliah is no more', he said. I was really sorry to hear the news.

We reached Pulliah's house. There were the familiar incantations freshly stencilled on the door to avert pestilence and misfortune, but the door was closed against me. I knocked several times and several people who had gathered around me shouted that Durra was there. The door was opened a few inches; a young man stood there, apparently to bar my way. I recognised the man as Pulliah's eldest son. He smiled faintly and said: 'Father always spoke to me about you.'

'Tell me about your father', I said.

Tears came into his eyes. 'They cut off his right hand, then they hacked off his left arm. They did that here', he said, pointing to a spot in front of the house.

'The Communists', he continued with a subdued anguish on his face, '... some things they wanted done he would not do. They thought he was dead and left him in a pool of blood.... I bound up his stumps with pieces of my dhoti and carried him on my back through the forest. I hid him one night in Venkaiah's house and he was in terrible agony.... I stole a bullock-cart and took him by the river path to the Mission Hospital at Ramanpet. The doctors said he was near death, then he regained consciousness for a while, said he wanted to die and he died the next day.'

The main street was empty and silent, but as I walked down it a few scavenger dogs, riddled with disease, were alternately barking and running in fright and a few children peered out of the doorways. I walked across the street to the little wayside shrine with its shapeless stone daubed with oil and red ochre. The old priest smiled toothlessly and came shambling out with palms pressed together in salutation. Emboldened by this, many villagers gathered around. Many of them I knew, but neither the Patwari nor the Deshmukh was there, since both had deserted their posts to live in the safety of the town twenty miles away. A herd of skinny cattle meandered down the street, raising a dense cloud of dust. I walked through a side-lane to the Dhedwada quarter where the Untouchables lived, now emancipated by law indeed but not yet accepted by their fellow-countrymen. They seemed to have sunk more deeply into poverty and degradation than when I had last seen them.

'Durra, Durra', cried someone from behind a nearby hut. Out came a woman, bowed low and touched my feet. It was Laxmi, a toothless old woman. I remembered her. I remembered too the night when I had heard of the illness of her grandson and had taken the lad to the hospital in my car.

Laxmi's action served as a signal and people came out of their huts and clustered around me, wildly jabbering.

'Just what is the trouble?' I asked.

'Durra, Durra', she cried passionately. 'We are hungry!'

There were cries and wails of assent to old Laxmi's declaration. I was surrounded by gaunt, drawn countenances which spoke of privation and near-starvation. 'Durra has come back', they cried. 'Durra has come back.'

Yes, they remembered me and it was touching. But it was painful to see that so little had been left of my years of labour. The lanes were heaped with refuse and ordure; cattle were back in the huts where families slept on the floors and my small school was derelict. In short, the village had reverted to type, for uplift work does not long survive the passing of a vigilant and interested officer. To change the habits of a people, to instil into them new ideas of health and hygiene, is the sustained work of many generations and cannot be imposed from without. To please a particular officer, the villagers may show a temporary zeal; but they go back to their old ways as soon as his back is turned. I told the people I had come to stay the night, and went with Ranga Rao to the Chowdi.

'Where is the Patwari? And the Deshmukh? And the Zamindar? Who tills their fields?'

'No one. They lie fallow', replied a lean bent greybeard whom I barely recognised as my fat cheerful friend, Ganuji.

'Ram Ram, Ganuji', I said, 'where are your two fine sons?'

Tears came into his eyes as he replied: 'The elder is in jail. The police suspected him of helping the Communists, though he was quite innocent.'

'And the younger?'

'He was kidnapped in daylight by the Communists. He went to the police headquarters to report the loss of his bicycle and they saw him there. I swear he never told the police anything.'

'Why not? If you don't help the police, how can they help you?'

'Durra, the police are helpless. If we gave them any information we should be killed outright and our boys kidnapped.'

'Wouldn't you like the police stationed in the village to protect you?'

'God forbid, never, never. If the police are billeted on us we shall have nothing left, and what use would they be? They don't know the countryside. They don't know the people. Often they don't even speak our language and just live off us without paying for it.'

'Do you see many subordinate officers?'

'Only in day time, and under police protection. So there is less begar (forced labour) nowadays. But we have nothing to eat, Durra. We are starving.'

That afternoon, the Patwari and the Deshmukh arrived, strongly escorted, on a hurried visit. I walked with them to the next village. There was nothing much to distinguish this village from other villages. The same strange half-acrid smell of baked earth and cow dung penetrated the nostrils, the same all-pervading dust greeted us. Outside, a shrieking mass of naked and half-naked children scrambled in the mud. Some people came out and gave us a bewildered look.

'What is all that about?' I asked a man, pointing to a house where a few men and women had collected.

'Oh, Narasimha's wife is going to have a baby.'

We saw an Untouchable daya, a mid-wife, clad in the dirty rags she wore for confinement. Her face and hands were clusters of festering sores. She was going to a tiny expectant mother, who, we were told, was a little girl-wife of thirteen or fourteen. While returning, I asked Vithal Rao, the Deshmukh: 'What news of that bright son of yours, who did so well at school?'

Vithal Rao answered without looking at me. 'He graduated and tried for a Government job, but he wasn't qualified.'

'I should have thought he was better qualified than most.'

'Oh no, he had no godfathers.'

'But I thought that was not important these days.'

90

'Oh yes, sir, it is, it is the same still; only different people count these days.'

This village consisted of a few hundred huddled huts with cakes of cow dung plastered to dry on the mud walls. Round the drinking well was stagnant filth. Dirty naked children, their bellies swollen by enlarged spleens, played in the refuse and mangy curs set up a deafening roar. Here, too, there was neither Patel nor Patwari nor any school, and here, too, were the same complaints and the same tales of woe.

'Why don't they at least rear some poultry?' I asked Vithal Rao. 'In my day the place was full of hens and eggs were cheap and plentiful: today I see not one.'

'I have tried it, but a single epidemic killed two hundred birds.'

'I don't mean large scale breeding of pedigree poultry, but the ordinary village hen. You never hear of them being wiped out by disease.'

'It's not worth their while keeping hens', said Vithal Rao, 'when every officer expects free chickens and eggs when he comes round on tour.'

'Do they still exact those tolls?'

Vithal Rao smiled. 'Our Tehsildar', he said, 'won a great reputation for honesty by paying publicly for all his supplies. But woe betide the unhappy Bania who forgot to return his money at the bottom of the basket!'

We returned to Venkatapur and the next day Ranga Rao and I set out, again by bullock-cart and bus, to the far end of the District, taking with us an old Patwari named Sita Ram. I was dismayed at what I had seen and I could think of nothing else. I was wondering why it was that these good and peaceful people had been involved in such terrible cruelty and violence. Had their poverty suddenly become intolerable? Were these the ways of desperation? Sita Ram was a sensible old man; I thought he ought to know the answer. But he wouldn't concede that poverty had anything to do with it.

'We were always poor, Sarkar; God, according to His own mysterious plan, made us so. But we didn't always do such things. No, Sarkar; it's not just that. I have seen a lot of the world. I have seen officers who took bribes and officers who were kind and honest. I have seen good times and bad and I tell you that today's troubles are due not to poverty but to wealth. I remember when we were far poorer, poorer than the labourers in a cotton factory now; still we were content with our religion and our simple pleasures. Now we are not. Why? Because we expect happiness to come with money. But we are wrong, for though we have more money we have less happiness. Oh, how happy we were in the old days, but it is all gone now.'

It was difficult to carry on a conversation amid the rattling noise and fearful jolting of the bullock-cart, so I decided to drive it myself. My passengers seemed doubtful of the wisdom of this, but the driver's seat over the axle with feet dangling behind the bullocks' tails is the best place in these vehicles and I preferred the risk of driving to the discomfort I was undergoing.

'Admit, Patwariji', I said, 'that you would be more comfortable in a motor-car with a skilful chauffeur.'

'No, Sarkar, no!' he chuckled. 'I am jolted now because you have lost the art of driving a bullock-cart. If you had remained a simple countryman I should now be resting in great ease.

'There will never be rest nor content in the world till you destroy your motorcars, telephones, wireless sets, newspapers. All discontent, all unhappiness, is due to your progress and knowledge. Wasn't that what Gandhiji said?' he asked.

'Well, not exactly, and it isn't quite as simple as you make out.'

'Believe me, invention should have stopped with the steam engine. That enables us to cover long distances at great speed and does no harm to anybody.'

At Malair, which was to be our headquarters for the next few days, Ranga Rao and I stayed at the dak bungalow while Sita Ram lodged in the village with a friend, Vasanth Rao. Vasanth Rao, a wiry little man, was a successful lawyer who had taken to politics from the very beginning. Like most people, he had his schooling with the Congress; but later, because of his strong Leftist views, he drifted away. He had been a fellow-traveller for some time; but when the Communist Party was banned he ceased to have anything to do with it. Many, however, suspected that he still had contacts with the Party and its underground; on much less suspicion others would have come to trouble, but not so Vasanth Rao. He had very influential friends still in the Congress Party who respected his intelligence and his integrity, and so the police dared not lay their hands on him till they had positive proof. He was looked at askance by the local politicians who knew that his association with the Congress Party really hung upon his friendship with individual leaders who liked him personally. Local Congressmen watched everything he did. For intelligence and political learning, Vasanth Rao was head and shoulders above the local leaders. Because of the peculiar position he occupied and the sharpness of his intellect, I knew he would understand my disinterested curiosity. Therefore I asked him if he could help me see anything that was happening. At first he was rather hesitant, mainly out of consideration for my personal safety; finally he agreed and took steps to ensure that we travelled in security, though he would not himself accompany us.

Early next day we drove through untilled fields and rough scrub jungle to Salampur. We were jolted and banged about; in defence we often alighted and walked ahead of the cart. Late that evening, having covered only fifteen miles, we came to the small village of Salampur. The burnt shells of houses, empty and broken grain baskets lying scattered among the matting and palm leaf shelters, bore witness to the disaster which had come upon the place. Gradually the people came out of hiding. The children were the filthiest I had ever seen, with thread-bare rags hanging around their spindly limbs. A few sick people lay on the bare floors of their huts, wrapped in ragged and dirty cotton sheets, their only bedding. There was no hospital within twenty-five miles and, even had there been one, nobody would have dared go there, for fear had robbed these people of all their strength, robbed them even of the desire to talk about their sufferings. The village officials visited the place only at the time of revenue collection and that too with a guard.

At last the Pujari of the temple was persuaded to tell us what had happened.

'There have been two raids within the last three months. Only a week ago, about a hundred jungli Koya tribesmen looted the village. Those whom they chose to slay, they slew after due warning. Death notices were posted on the Patel's and the Bania's doors a full three weeks before the raiders came upon us, warning them even when and how they would be killed.'

'Didn't the police come?'

'Certainly they came, but only after it was all over. And what the Communists left, the police stole! What good could they do? Nobody dared make a report. Now the village is dead, for those who can leave have left, and those who remain do not trouble to till the fields. Why should they, since the crops will all be devoured either by the Communists or by the police?'

'Do they never catch these gangs or their leaders?'

'Two leaders have been caught in the last twelve months, and they have escaped by bribing the police.'

'What are these Koyas and other aboriginals up to?' I asked Ranga Rao. 'Don't tell me they've ever heard of Communism or any other "ism".'

'Maybe not, but they follow anyone who promises them loot.'

93

On our way back we met Vasanth Rao. He was obviously in a hurry, but stopped to ask us if we should like to attend a Burra Katha (village drama). Of course we were keen on doing so, for we had heard of these propaganda plays.

'At Laxmipuram, six miles due north', he said. 'Midnight, behind the temple.'

Ranga Rao and I had chosen to ride the last few miles and were just alighting from the cart when a group of about six men suddenly came into view and a man who appeared to be their leader shoved a lighted torch into my face. We were ordered to stand still. This self-appointed committee of inspection of nocturnal visitors moved off a short space, held a muffled conference, came over and, with the aid of their torches, scanned us again. Then the leader rifled my dispatch case while the other man held a light. Without a word the man threw the dispatch case back into the cart and then all of them sauntered away.

We arrived quite an hour before the appointed time, but nobody took any notice of us. The village was all silent and dark and a general air of inertia seemed to pervade everything. There were no signs of the Burra Katha party. But within a quarter of an hour of midnight about a hundred and fifty people had collected and soon the show started with songs. These were all of a Communist flavour, ringing the changes on the stock Marxist themes. The crowd appeared to be nervous. People showed little of the pleasurable anticipation which usually precedes such performances.

After the songs were over two men opened the proceedings. The prologue went something like this:

First Actor: Comrades, they prate to us of property and law. Property is the loot of thieves. Law is the rule of tyrants.

Second Actor: As the sun shines equally on all mankind, so shall the workers inherit equally the earth.

First Actor: March, Comrades, to cast down your oppressors. Seize what they have stolen from you.

Second Actor: The rich and the proud shall be butchered like goats and the horny feet of the toiler shall splash in the blood of kings.

The Chorus always repeated: 'March, Comrades, to cast down your oppressors.'

After the monotone recital of the prologue came a single lengthy act, cleverly recounting a tale of ancient India: the story of a tyrant monarch who lived a frivolous life of luxury

94

and ease at the expense of his poor subjects. A brave and pious guru dared to reproach the slothful king in public for his perverse misrule and, of course, he was sentenced to death. At the last moment the people rose in rebellion, rescued the guru and imprisoned the oppressor.

The greater part of the play consisted of long speeches by the guru and the proletarian rebels, partly in the usual Marxist jargon, and partly couched in the philosophy of Mahatma Gandhi to plant the message more deeply in the hearts and minds of the audience. I remember vividly the Gandhian touch in the speeches of the guru when he had pardoned the king.

He declaimed: 'You want me to take up the duties of ruling over these people so that I may leave a name for posterity? You want me to live in this gilded palace? This is not for me, my son. What is wealth? What is fame? Tell me in which year immortality begins and I'll trouble myself about fame. Wealth: ten gold coins, a thousand, a million? Tell me how much the world can be bought for and I will labour for wealth. The difference, my son, between poverty and riches, between oblivion and fame, is so slight that it is not worth my lifting a finger for it. ... Forget the past and build a new future and live in the hearts of the people. ...'

The play ended just before dawn and we slipped away. We reached Malair tired out and longing only for sleep.

In the evening, Vasanth Rao asked me how we had liked the Burra Katha.

'It was a strange mixture', I said. 'They started off with bloodthirsty songs of hate and revenge and ended with soul-force and non-violence.'

'Of course', said Ranga Rao, 'in the end any Government must rely on brute-force, not soul-force. But need you mix up these two incompatibles quite so blatantly?'

'These', said Vasanth Rao, 'are some old forms with a new theme and new songs. Unless the plot has a mythological or religious basis, people take no interest in it. One must sugar-coat the pill.'

Later in the evening, there arrived Father Mallia, the Indian Catholic missionary. He was both a friend and opponent of mine of long standing, whom I liked and respected, though I had remained impervious to all his attempts to convert me. He delighted in argument and kept his temper in the most Christian manner, however much one provoked him. Educated in Madras and widely travelled in America and Australia, he was the best type of Christian missionary one could find. His hospital at

Ramanapet is the only one of its kind in the District and the poor and oppressed of all faiths turn to him for help, though the new bureaucracy is vehemently anti-missionary.

Like the priestly characters of Balzac he was built big; his body seemed a balloon of protuberant masses. As he laboriously lowered himself into a low cane chair (for the act of sitting as performed by him was no ordinary affair but a prolonged process), it creaked and groaned in protest. He began puffing away at a pungent Trichinopoly cheroot, presenting the appearance of a Brahminy bull squatting in mid-street.

'We are talking about the Communists', I said.

'Indeed?' The Padre cocked a bushy eyebrow at Vasanth Rao. 'Then I am sure you are very ... well informed.'

'You seem to be well informed yourself, Padre Sahib', said Vasanth Rao with a smile.

'Tolerably, tolerably. I keep my ear to the ground and hear Satan's footsteps when he walks abroad.'

'Satan?' asked Vasanth Rao.

'Satan', the Padre repeated with an emphatic nod. 'Satan in the guise of arrogance, cruelty and intolerance. If people only obeyed the two great commandments ... love thy God and love thy neighbour as thyself ... the world's problems would simply cease to exist.'

'Is your work affected by the revolt?' I asked.

'Of course. Whose isn't? Try as you will to keep out of politics, you can't ignore this turmoil. It is true that very few Christians have joined the Communists, if they can be called Communists, but there is much sympathy among our young men with the declared objects of these people, if not with their methods.'

'Don't you consider the rebels to be Communists?'

'What do our simple peasants know of Communism? Or the terrorists themselves, for that matter? They just roam from village to village not so much preaching a creed as collecting money for themselves. They loot the landowners and the shop keepers and tell the villagers: "These have oppressed you in the past; now it is the time for vengeance." They visit villages and hold courts and divide the village land amongst the landless, marking the boundaries of the new allotments with red flags before going away. If the landowner insists on his rights or complains to the Government he is murdered, so nobody dare oppose them.'

'But what do they achieve by burning villages and murdering innocent people, peasants like themselves?'

'Terror, money and prestige. They catch a few well-to-do

96

people, squeeze money out of them and make them salute the red flag seven times. These victims, if they survive, generally leave their villages and go to the towns, so their land is seized. It is true that the landless peasant generally does not want the land because he is afraid of what may befall him, and is as a rule very ill-equipped as a cultivator, but the Communist has won his point. Then the rebels announce, "If any of you owe a debt to the Pattadar or to the Bania, repudiate it. If they demand their debt, beat them, cut them to pieces." A thing like this does appeal to a debt-ridden peasant, but the next week brings the police and the revenue officials to restore the *status quo* and, incidentally, to eat up anything that is left; and that's where the Government goes wrong. They ought to realise that if there was one thing which the Communists did that was right it was to show that the *status quo* was too oppressive to continue in a democratic age. When our leaders realise this, the back of what little real Communism there is in all this part of the world will be broken. But it is not yet so. Meanwhile, no villager will give information to the police because he is afraid of reprisals and has lost faith in Government. If he does not cultivate the land allotted to him, the Communists punish him for sabotage, so the poor devil is under fire from all sides.'

'I wonder if these gangs have a central organisation, and run a parallel government of some sort?'

'There is no government as such, though some of them do belong to the Communist Party. Most of them are local badmashes, and many Koya and Hill Reddi tribesmen join them for loot. They have some sort of organisation and issue their own news sheets. The party men, the few real Communists, do the propaganda in villages, build jungle strong-points, make crude bombs and other weapons, set up their village intelligence service and above all spread disorder.'

'Padre Sahib', said Ranga Rao, 'I am a simple man and I still do not see why people who aim at bettering the lot of the workers should set out to terrorise and impoverish them.'

'Their aim is to provoke a patient people to revolt. When terrorism disrupts all the normal transactions of life and chaos continues long enough, any change can be only for the better. They want to make an intolerable world worse than before, to make living conditions so hard that the people will become ripe for "mass action"!'

'I wonder if anybody knows where the leaders live?'

'Some of them live in big towns or work in the coalfields. Many live undetected in the villages right under the noses of the police. They have an efficient intelligence system, and the police and the army, lumbering along roads and tracks, cannot catch them.'

After the Padre had gone, Ranga Rao said: 'Do you think he was right in saying that nothing founded on hate can last?'

'The Communist', I replied, 'will not admit that his regime is founded on hate. What we call hate, he would claim to be vehemence of compassion. He and his like possess the ferocity of crusaders and the zeal of evangelists. When a cause becomes holy, look out! Its methods become vile.'

'Quite so, and for that reason Communism can maintain itself only during the struggle for power. Once success is achieved, once the rebel becomes the ruler and has to deliver the goods he has promised, Communism decays and perishes.'

By now, my appetite for first-hand experiences had been whetted. I had learnt something of the general organisation of the Communist bands in other areas; but here I was particularly keen on seeing the impact of this most modern of the fanaticisms of human thought on an aboriginal people. Ranga Rao would have none of it; and it was certainly a risky affair, in fact, fool-hardy, because we should certainly be mistaken for officials or spies. But I was determined and Ranga Rao finally yielded and agreed that we might try and get just to the outskirts of Koya territory.

We went by jeep. Nowhere can the prowess of this vehicle be seen better than in this rough, mainly forest, Koya country. There was no road where we went; we had to follow gullies and cart tracks. But no terrain is impossible for the jeep. The country was undulating. We traversed the foot-hills, the small hillocks which are the vanguard of the main Ghats further east. So favourable is this terrain to the terrorists that they are commonly called 'Gutta Durralu', hill masters, by the villagers.

For a few miles everything looked more or less normal, but we had not far to go before we came into the troubled zone. The country seemed deserted and cattle were grazing in fields where jawar had been harvested. We had to make a long detour to avoid a bridge which had been dismantled. Masonry had been knocked off one of the pillars; it looked as though the rebels had been driven off by a police patrol before they could fill the holes with explosives to blow up the whole bridge.

As we entered the forest, we found that a tree had been felled across the road. We drove around it and, after by-passing several more roadblocks, came to a village whose inhabitants started running away when they saw us. We sat quietly in the car and after half an hour they began to venture back. They all seemed extremely nervous and it took some time before most of the men, and even a few women, collected around us.

'Why did you run away?' I asked.

'Sarkar, we thought you were a police party.'

'People with clear consciences do not run away from the police.'

'We only wish to be left in peace, Durra, but our brothers in the jungle tell us that the Government has declared war on all Koyas and will kill any Koya who is caught.'

'The Government will not punish you unless you help the rebels.'

'If we do not help them, Durra, the rebels will burn our houses and kill us. Mallaraju's men lie in the jungle only a few miles away, and he is a very terrible man. Moreover, he is nearer to us than the police.'

'Who is this Mallaraju?' I asked Ranga Rao.

'He is the son of a Koya Patwari, an educated man who seems to be the leader of the rebellion hereabouts.'

'Ranga Rao, I should like to meet this Mallaraju. Let's find his "army".'

'Nonsense!'

'It's not nonsense. We are neither officials nor capitalists and we have no money. Why should he harm us? All we want is to learn the facts and, if he is an intelligent man, he'll see he has far more to gain by treating us well than by murdering us.'

It was a full hour before Ranga Rao gave way. And after another long argument, and the disbursement of a good many rupees, three villagers agreed to guide us to the rebel camp.

We left the car and marched by a tortuous track through fields and patches of forest. Every furlong or so the track was blocked by felled trees. At a stream, the Sangam Vagu, we were held up for about an hour until we found someone able to guide us.

It was getting on for dusk, a time at which even the most ordinary of surroundings assume a mysterious air and the shadows hang not only on the ground but in the mind. According to Hindu mythology, the Lord had once promised a demon that he would be killed neither by day nor by night; so that when he had ultimately to be destroyed, he was killed when it was neither day nor night. Such was this hour when a murky sterility hung over everything and it struck me that even metaphysically these were indeed such times when there was neither darkness nor light. I confess I felt a chill passing down my spine. I suddenly realised what a foolish thing we had done. I, who by my very appearance could be seen to be an official by these people, had ventured into an area which was no man's land. Life was cheap here and a tiny bit of lead could end my life, for what it was worth, here in Koya land. And poor Ranga Rao had been dragged into all this. To distract my mind from these dismal thoughts I kept looking about and trying to locate where we were. We were walking through a small valley between two steep hillocks which were covered with thick foliage. Here was an excellent spot for an ambush, I thought, and, as if guessing my thoughts, my guide informed me just then that the District Superintendent of Police and his party had been attacked at the very spot a few days before. As we turned, I saw in the distance, right at the very top of the hillock on our right, a building that seemed to be hanging dangerously over the cliff. I was sure that from there one could see for miles around. It was the tomb of a Muslim saint, our guide informed us, now used as an outpost by Mallaraju's men. It was so close to thick forest that if a police patrol of any strength attempted to approach it, the terrorists could easily disappear into the jungle. The guide showed us the path that would lead to that place but refused to accompany us any further. In case we turned out to be spies, he did not want to be recognised by Mallaraju's men. There was nothing we could do, for before we could argue the guide just disappeared into the forest. We had hardly walked a few furlongs along the path when we were surrounded suddenly by about six or seven Koyas who seemed to spring from nowhere. They wore typical Koya dress, a mere strip of cloth a few inches wide and a few feet long tied across the waist.

The Koyas listened as we told them why we had come. They betrayed no reaction. They merely took us to the building we had seen from the distance and there we spent the night. They ate roti, unleavened bread, made of jawar and drank a native brew which smelled horribly. They offered us the roti and the brew, too. They were quite jovial and hospitable but they were always alert and suspicious. When we said we had come all the way to see Mallaraju they said in a very ominous manner that we should be seeing him whether we liked it or not.

Next morning, we saw a small group of people carrying water into the forest. Obviously they were on their way to Mallaraju's camp, so we followed them. After about an hour, we came upon many men sitting around camp fires. Although surprised, no one tried to stop us. Then we came to a place where some young men were doling out grain and other supplies in exchange for written orders (coupons) issued by Mallaraju. As we walked on, we saw a sentry—not a Koya—who carried a rifle and was dressed in khaki shorts and puttees. As soon as he stopped us, he blew a whistle and ran up the hill. We followed him but were accosted by several men, one of whom carried a twelve-bore gun and an automatic pistol.

'That is Mallaraju', said our guide.

Mallaraju was short and stocky, with a heavy look. He came from peasant stock; he was not an intellectual like Aggi Reddi. In any village he would have been unidentifiable among ordinary people. But there was an alertness about him : not in the sparkle of his eye, like Aggi Reddi's, but in his general bearing and behaviour and in the sharp glances which he cast round. He was like a deer in that split second between its suspicion of approaching danger and its act of springing to safety. Mallaraju had adopted as his permanent bearing just that knife-edge alertness that nature usually gives only at times of imminent danger. Probably this was because he was always in danger. It was said that he could put his ear to the ground and by the sound detect the numbers of an approaching enemy patrol. The only hint of fierceness and cruelty about him was his widely dilated nostrils; one could almost imagine them breathing fire. He had all the vitality, the primordial vigour and the animal magnetism that exists in a state of nature. But he had none of the placid majesty of a tiger; he was, in spite of his solidity, more like the alert and cunning panther and, like the panther, he kept you guessing about when he would spring on you.

Mallaraju scowled at us but made no hostile move.

'Ram Ram', I said, and he replied with clenched fist salute.

'What are you doing here?' he said. 'We make short work of spies.'

'I am not a spy', I said, 'nor an official of any kind. I have come to see and to hear from your own lips what your aims are and what you are fighting for. So far, I have only heard evil of you from your enemies.'

Mallaraju seemed pleased at the implied flattery and spoke in a low voice to some of his comrades. These, the leaders of the rebellion, were not aboriginals at all. The oldest was a Brahmin and the sentry we had first seen, like several other khaki-clad young men of Mallaraju's 'Headquarters staff', seemed to be an ex-soldier. Several of these had a smattering of English.

Finally, he turned to us and said: 'I shall make inquiries about you. Meanwhile you are under arrest, but I shall not have you bound unless you try to escape.'

We were able to wander about with some freedom and see what was going on, though the leaders did not like us talking to anyone outside their own circle. There were about fifty non-Koyas armed with modern firearms, a few muzzle-loaders and a large number of Koyas armed with bows and arrows. We saw several baskets filled with oval shaped objects the size of large coconuts. One of the ex-soldiers, obviously to impress us, picked up one of them from a basket and threw it into the forest, where it exploded with a terrific bang. No doubt these country bombs were useful to them for terrorising a raided village.

We heard that the guerillas were getting their ammunition from Kondawada and their supplies from Pantur and other towns. The Koyas are not politically-minded, but there were also in the camp a good many non-Koya Communists from the collieries who, when spoken to, replied in the usual Marxist jargon. There were also men from other parts of the country, including a sadhu from Kathiawar. Among the leaders, some wore military tunics and assumed a tone of authority and these appeared to have been well-trained by the organisers. For instance, when I asked some of them whether a group of men were Koyas or Hill Reddis, they replied that such differences were of no account since all were brother-workers. Many of the guerillas were mere boys who should have been at school. The rebels seemed to have introduced a regular system of conscription. Every household had to provide one man for their service, on pain of having the house looted and burned. The tribal laws and the tribal habit of giving unquestioning obedience to the headman helped this sort of organisation in this area.

Having once had a good deal of influence with the Koyas (for as a junior officer I had been employed at weaning them from the jungle and settling them as agriculturists), I tried to talk to them privately; but this was not possible for whenever I was with a group of Koyas one of Mallaraju's men would join us to guard against disaffection.

We were fed with jawar bread and dhal and were not badly treated, but after the third day in the jungle Ranga Rao said: 'I thought, Sahib, the rebels would murder us, but instead it seems we shall die of boredom. I can't stand any more of this. Let's walk out.'

'All right. I don't suppose they'll stop us. For all they know, we'll just have gone for a stroll in the jungle.'

So, in the evening, on the pretext of an innocent walk, we set off in the direction of the river, hoping to find a boat to take us across to the government-held territory on the other side.

After half an hour or so we thought we had got clean away. But soon three khaki-clad youths came up and joined us. They chatted quite amicably, but they were armed with rifles and knives, and when they suggested that it was time to go back for supper we had perforce to agree.

Mallaraju made no comment on the incident, but from this time onwards two or three guards were always with us.

On the fifth day of our captivity, Vasanth Rao arrived.

'My dear Sahib', he said, 'and Ranga Rao, too. Really, this is an unexpected pleasure. But you must not do it again, not again.'

'Do what?' I asked.

'Poke your noses in where you aren't wanted. Our friend Mallaraju wants to soak you in kerosene and set light to you as spies, but I have persuaded him that you are harmless.'

'Surely Marx wouldn't have objected to a more humane form of disposing of counter-revolutionaries', I said with some heat, half in jest and half from real disgust.

I could see that Vasanth Rao winced at this. 'You don't understand, Rihaz Sahib', he said. 'This is not Communism. Unfortunately, our cause has got mixed up here with a tribal revolt and with all the sadism that goes with tribal vengeance. Some of us cannot stand the way this fellow runs this show. But unfortunately, for the present, he is getting away with it and he has the upper hand. Some of our own comrades sitting in Bombay visualise this as the grand Telangana revolt. It is not the time now. Of course, unlike you, I'll never say that theirs was not a glorious chapter in our Telangana struggle. But this is not it. That was in the other District. Just go there and see what the people think of us! We have given them land, given them security and, above all, given them human dignity. But some of us feel that this affair should stop at once, because men like Mallaraju are doing harm to our cause. Further, political conditions have changed and we shall not be able to rally the people against the new regime as we did against the former feudal regime. This is bound to lead to confusion and the ideological disarmament of the masses. No, this certainly is not what we approve of, and I am sure that before long the higher-ups in the party will also realise this and condemn it. But don't imagine that I am recommending calling off what we have achieved in the agrarian revolution which the party itself completed in the other Districts. That we shall always defend. But Mallaraju, remember, is basically an anarchist; he is not a party leader. Anyway, while the going is good, please get away from them. I am returning this evening. Come away with me.'

8   What has happened?

AFTER I returned from my wanderings I set myself to review the entire situation. It was strange how in these villages, amid all the violence and confusion, the traditional rituals and festivals still continued. Bandits might rob. Police might oppress. Land revenue and grain levies might be crushing in their incidence. The Deshmukh and the Jagirdar might remain remote and unsympathetic. But even so, month after month crawled by, marked by the great feast days, by weddings and funerals, by the daily worship in the temple, by the nightly tipple in the toddy shop. Yes, I thought, I was finding myself back where I had started in some of my original thinking about my own people. I had always imagined that I had known them. They are simple; their minds are easy to read. They lead a life at the very brink of existence, whence poverty did not permit them to wander far. The world has not given them enough of the things of life on which to erect the vast superstructure of creative thought and the habits of civilisation. Their minds are not cluttered with the complexities of modern living. I had prided myself that I could always tell what their actions and reactions would be. To me they had always appeared a patient peaceful people upon whose powers of endurance nature seemed to have set no limits. They ask nothing of life but the barest existence.

They are shy and reserved; but if one can speak their dialect and gain their confidence, one finds beneath the dull exterior a lively disposition, a love of fun and gossip. Completely illiterate, they are isolated from the outside world. Through lack of understanding and experience, they distrust any constructive measures to improve their lot. To the vast majority of them, Government means merely taxes and oppression by the landlord or the police.

They undergo endless hardships, but their minds still live in a world of song and fable. They are victims of their own fatalism. The fetters of social usage and tradition still constrain them to be a rather lazy, improvident, under-nourished and un-ambitious people. They cannot discern in the ashes of a dying society the phoenix of the new order. In fact, they are not in the habit of looking ahead at all; the problems of today hardly permit them to bother about the morrow. Such was my view of them. It seemed to me that fatalism and a sense of impotence had corroded their will-power and devitalised even their humblest ambitions.

Yet today I feel that my estimates were wrong. These very peasants, for whom I had thought suffering could have no limits, had revolted. The very foundations of my thought, my social analysis, had been shattered. Where had I erred in my reading of these people? No matter how much I reflect, I cannot change my judgment about the people as individuals. I was right there; and yet in the collective sense, in the reaction of these people as a group to the problems that had been heaped upon them, I seem to have erred completely. That error had lain in neglecting the great proviso of all scientific laws—'other things being equal'. These people, whom I had loved and whom I fancied I knew so well, could have gone on reacting to the problems of their various indi-vidual lives in the manner which I should have expected them to react, 'other things being equal'. But, fortunately or unfortunately, other things had not continued to be equal. I had known these people as individuals; I had known their problems as the problems of individuals. I had perhaps left out of my calculations the fact that they formed part of a stratum of society; I had perhaps over-looked the possibility that their individual reactions could be affected by stresses and strains in that society and by a state of flux in its various strata. I had not allowed for the fact that when what is without impinges on what is within, changes within take place as a matter of course. What then had happened during my absence? It was not that the people had suddenly gone over to Satan and become vile and violent, but that certain forces, which had not been there before, had entered the social structure.

In the cities there lived the rich, in mediaeval pomp and splendour; rich by the accident of birth and jealous of their power and privilege. But they were of all the blindest, incapable of reading the signs of the times, clinging to a past that was effete and outdated. They led frivolous and fanciful lives, cut off from reality and oblivious to the overpowering changes tak-ing place around them. They believed in the pursuit of pleasure as an end in itself and indulged in it with artistic abandon. In times past they had built up in the country an island of culture so luscious and beautiful, so harmonious a blend of so many influences, that to this day people find in it the apotheosis of both the East and the West. They were generous and chivalrous even to a fault and their hospitality became a tradition in itself. Everyone was welcome here, everyone who was an adventurer or soldier of fortune, poet or philosopher, saint or sufi, artist or architect. And yet on whose shoulder did the burden fall? It fell on the peasant. For this was a society of men with no social vision, living on the toil of the peasant, striving to hold on to power or rather to the idleness which was, for them, the purpose of power.

And so it would have continued, a society with all its contradictions of utmost refinement and crudest oppression, of generosity and extortion, of graceful living and sordid poverty, had other things been equal. But the world around was not static; it was in the throes of a vast national and social upheaval.

'All land belongs to Gopal ... where, then, is the boundary line? Man is the maker of that line and he can, therefore, unmake it. Gopal, in modern language, is the state, the people ... land and all property is his who will work it.' Thus said the Mahatma. In the context of the feudal conditions and in the context of outdated notions of governance the Mahatma might easily have been a Communist.

Here there had never been a class which could, strictly speaking, be called the middle class; there was, therefore, no intelligentsia of the kind which could claim the heritage of Jefferson and Adam Smith and demand equal rights for all in land as in other things. The peasant was kind, simple and contented till political ambition and passion for power, disguised as communal hatred, finally blasted the walls of isolation. The little men with little minds were unequal to the demands of the times, and the pressure from outside was irresistible. Thus, other things no longer remained equal, and all my readings of the simple peasant's mind went awry. In the resultant uncertainty, flux and bewilderment, the Communist entered upon the scene to promise the peasant plenty and happiness in a new world in which he would be the master. The way which the Communist showed might have been wrong, the direction misleading, the goal itself fraudulent; yet the self-confidence of the Communist was the only light which pierced the surrounding gloom. The peasant knew little of the price which must be paid for the new world; moreover, he felt, in any case, that the price would be paid by others in a currency which he had never possessed. He wanted land and the fruits of his toil for himself. He was an individualist *par excellence*. All that he wanted was to live by the sweat of his brow. It could be said of him, as it was said of an English village, 'that no class in the community has so beaten and crushed history. It was a life without hope. Let others call him a free man; he knew well enough that he was another man's slave. For him there was no hope of better things. However hard he worked, it was for somebody else; however skilfully he sowed, another reaped.' Whatever the language and whatever the form in which he fought against such an order, it must perforce be remembered that the peasant was only fighting for the overthrow of oppressive feudal vestiges and for his right to live in justice and freedom.

In the face of this onslaught, the sheer march of events, the hybrid structure of society, which had decayed and outlived its utility, crumbled. At this point the middle class intelligentsia, whatever its strength, had achieved its purpose: it had cried halt. But would the Communist take heed? No, of course not: to him, the goal was farther still. The people themselves, the sons of the soil, had a quarrel only with oppression and insecurity. They had set out to assert their right to live, not to justify the teachings of Marx. The calm and quiet atmosphere of yesterday, however, was suddenly shattered amid mortar bursts and whining bullets. The problems of ages could no longer be left unsolved. Those in power thought that they could fight this upsurge with arms and ammunition. Can a social and economic problem be solved by armies and police? Not that I know of. At best, they can hold the ring while the battle against poverty and ignorance is fought by other men and by other methods.

Epilogue by the Editor

HAD been away from India for several years and during this time I was too busy to bring together Rihaz's notes dealing with a small corner of India, a country in the birth pangs of her independence. Now, however, after I have had time to go through them, I decided to revisit Venkatapur, the centre of Rihaz's early work and the feudal city where he lived, and to see the changes since his day.

I landed in Bombay in the afternoon. The well-known patient faces, the familiar sounds and odours, places half-remembered, crowded in upon my senses in swift succession, blurring into each other. I was buffeted by memories and wanted time to sort out my feelings.

Meeting my host Hannu Khan at the airport was a real joy. It was always a delight to talk to him: a man generous, widely read and travelled, an economist and an administrator, always affectionate and sincere, with whom one could disagree without loss of respect or liking. Khan and I had worked together in the same service and we were glad to meet after many years. On our way to his flat we made general conversation, feeling our way back to our old friendship. The crowds leisurely crossing the roads, the honking of horns, the busy pan-shops on the wayside, the crammed buses, and I knew that I was back home.

Khan had a comfortable flat facing the sea. His family was away and we had it to ourselves. Khan was a great gourmet and his Goanese cook produced an excellent Indian dinner: prawn curry, long well-cooked rice, paratas and kababs, pickles and almond sweets. We planned my three days in Bombay: one I had promised to spend with the Mumjis, who were to return the next afternoon from their holiday; the other two I wanted to roam about meeting old friends.

The next day happened to be an official holiday and, at a late breakfast, we were joined by our mutual friend, Bhandari, who taught economics at a local College.

Casually I asked Khan about the idea behind the Muslim Convention* then being discussed in the newspapers.

'So far as I am concerned there is not, and there should not be, any problem of minorities in a secular and democratic country like ours, but, of course, we have our share of bigots.'

'Such as?'

'People still distinguish in India between a Raman and a Rahman† and so long as we live in the past, fear and suspicion are bound to haunt the minorities and threaten the work of Gandhi and Nehru. *I* don't feel a second or a third class citizen of India but I know many who do. To me, this is as much my country as anybody else's and I'm quite prepared to fight for it. I know there is nothing more humiliating or hurting than to become a suspect in one's own country but patience is needed. Nehru is trying to change all that. The Convention, I take it, will convey a protest, but whether that will do any good is anybody's guess . . . it may actually do more harm.'

Bhandari intervened: 'The problem *does* exist. Let's not be blind to it and imagine that we shall solve it by a few consoling speeches. We've been pretending for the last twelve years that it doesn't exist, but it does. Make communalism a penal offence, a crime against the state . . . I wouldn't mind if they hanged a few fanatics to improve the manners of the rest.'

'My dear Bhandari', said Khan, 'you cannot change hearts by hanging. I believe time alone can wipe out mutual distrust.'

'But what has the Government done to change hearts beyond throwing the minorities a few crumbs here and there?' asked Bhandari. 'That's not enough. Let them come down with a heavy hand.' He banged the table hard and, when the plates stopped rattling, added: 'The majority can afford to be generous. Can't they?'

Mumji lived in the same apartment, still quite well-to-do even though he was no longer a director of several companies.

'I am a gentleman-at-large, enjoying life as it comes', he said. He appeared reconciled to living on his capital which, I imagined, was not inconsiderable.

Shanta, his wife, had grown grey gracefully and had lost neither her charm nor her interest in politics. She was still work-

---

* The nationalist Muslims of India held a Convention to draw Government attention to some of their grievances.

† Raman is a Hindu name; Rahman is Muslim.

ing hard, with zeal and dedication, organising charities for orphanages, homes for destitute women and the aged and the blind. Those who helped her in the many tasks she undertook were, according to her husband, mostly the fashionable and ambitious wives of officials and businessmen. In their blowing, hand-woven silk saris and foreign make-up, duly accompanied by a photographer from a society magazine, they occasionally visited the villages to teach child care and modern cuisine to peasant women with large families and no kitchen stoves.

That afternoon the Mumjis gave a lunch party, and to it came Bhandari, the economics lecturer, and Hiralal, Mumji's brother-in-law. The conversation turned to new books and authors. When Hiralal mentioned a book on Marx by a professor in Mexico, Mumji impatiently interrupted: 'For heaven's sake!' he said. 'Anyone can prove, by picking and choosing his texts, that Jesus was the first Marxist—pardon!—the second. The Buddha was the first, wasn't he? Or that when Marx writes about the false and artificial needs of man he was simply quoting Jesus, or Mohammed, who declared "poverty is my pride".'

'Does it prove anything?' asked Shanta calmly. 'These fellows want to establish what Marx really meant. G. D. H. Cole hadn't an inkling. If Marx's teaching contains some of the greatest thought of the world, irrespective of whether it comes from the Buddha, Christ, Mohammed, Spinoza, Goethe or Hegel, it only strengthens the thesis of Erich Fromm, or whatever his name was.'

After lunch we started talking of important events in India during the last ten years.

'It was folly to talk of unity', said Bhandari, 'and then to divide up the country by language. If a rearrangement was necessary we should have deliberately created multi-lingual states on a regional basis. Linguistic states are already fighting over boundaries, water rights, the location of oil refineries or steel factories, to say nothing of local languages themselves, without the least interest in the country as a whole. Is not each State building its own centre of power? It is said that we were committed to linguistic divisions before we gained independence but the Government got cold feet when one man in a State fasted unto death because he wanted a linguistic State to be created. . . . There are people who say the old man didn't want to die!'

'Now, now, that's not fair', Mumji shouted.

'The whole idea was wrong. To whom was the commitment made? To ourselves? Our leaders should have the courage *now* to repudiate the idea', said Hiralal.

They were probably still arguing after I left.

The narrow street leading up to Jhaveri Bazaar from Crawford Market was so full of pedestrians, push-carts, bicycles, cars, lorries and bullock-carts that it was difficult to move. People were jostling each other, the motorists kept up a constant honking and the drivers of other vehicles went on shouting at the pedestrians to move out of their way. There were loud invitations to step into every shop.

'Come right in, Sahib, please—we have everything you are looking for.'

I was accosted by a ragged fruit vendor. 'Wonderful figs, you won't get them anywhere.'

'No, I don't want any figs.'

He begged: 'Just see them, you can't get such beauties anywhere.'

'I don't want them.'

'Just see them.'

They really looked fresh and good. 'How much', I asked.

'Three rupees a dozen.'

I thought they were cheap. I could have haggled but the crowd was pushing. So, paying him the three rupees, I took my dozen figs. Then I saw that the top three were all that I got for my money as the rest were rotten. I knew there was little to be gained now from argument and neither had I the time for it. So clutching my rotten figs I moved on.

A boy rushed towards me, imploring: 'Please, may I clean your shoes?'

My shoes were clean enough, I thought, but the emaciated urchin in rags was almost begging. I joined the patient queue at the edge of the pavement. I asked: 'What do you earn a day?'

'Eight annas a day', he said, looking at me with obvious sadness in his eyes.

'Is all this yours?' I asked, pointing at the tins of polish and the other tools of his trade.

'No', he said in a tone that showed no bitterness, 'all this belongs to the Seth.' He pointed to the line of shoe-shines. 'All of us are employed by the Seth, who pays us a wage depending upon the number of pairs we clean.'

I paid him eight annas for his work. He looked at me unbelievingly and a gleam came into his eyes.

'Your shoes are good; do you come from a foreign country?'

'Why?'

'Only foreigners pay so much. Thank you.'

Somebody bumped against me; obviously he was in a hurry. A woman carrying a heavy head-load dropped it on my shoulders.

I dodged and she passed on as if nothing had happened. Another woman who was collecting cattle droppings screamed as she was nearly run over by a car.

A man with his push-cart asked me if I wanted any buttons or neckties. Before I could refuse another man touched me on the shoulder and whispered: 'Want a nice fountain-pen, cheap, very cheap?' I indicated that I did not want any. 'See, it is genuine. Want a Swiss watch?'

I walked past him. Somebody called: 'Please step in. We have nice pullovers for you.'

I did not want any and paid no attention to him. Another man came running towards me. 'I'll take you to a good shop where you can get very cheap pullovers.' 'No, I don't want pullovers', I said definitely. 'What else do you want? I'll show you good shops, cheap shops.'

I got rid of him. The shouting and the commotion were everywhere; a small boy was knocked down by a slow-moving bicycle. There were mutual accusations but the crowd took little notice. I began to think that I had never seen such a mobile muddle of humanity, so many people moving, shouting, spitting on the pavements and on the street. The stench of urine and perspiration was intense.

A cloth shop looked clean and I thought of seeking momentary refuge. I had hardly stepped in when a most cordial welcome boomed: 'Come in, come in. What would you like to have?'

'I want a dozen white handkerchiefs.'

'Handkerchiefs, sorry, we keep no handkerchiefs. Perhaps you might like to see something else?'

A middle-aged man with a beak nose and thinning hair, sitting in one corner of the shop reading the *Times of India*, peered over his glasses and said: 'If you wish, I shall give you an address where you can get handkerchiefs; it is quite near.' Then he looked me up and down and said: "You come from abroad?'

'Why do you think I do?'

'The cut and quality of your clothes show that you come from America, perhaps.'

'Yes, I was there for some years.'

'What do the Americans think of India?'

I meekly offered an opinion: 'They think India is a great democracy, a great republic.'

'Do they know we are socialistic too?'

I stared at him. 'You know', he said, 'we are a socialistic, democratic republic: one country, one party and one leader.' And there were shadows of anger moving behind his eyes.

Before I could attempt to say anything he buried himself again in his paper. He had lost interest in me.

As I left the shop, a man volunteered to show me a place where I could get handkerchiefs and, though I declined his offer, he stuck to me like a leech and guided me into a dark lane which had only cloth shops. Veiled women were selecting saris by electric light; parents were leisurely discussing trousseaus for their girls. I did not know where I was being led, for the lane looked unending and the stench increased with every step. Abruptly I turned back, running the gauntlet of invitations from every shop I passed, followed by my self-appointed guide protesting loudly.

I could get rid of him only by paying four annas.

It was a relief to come out on to the main street again, even though there were more people, more stray cattle, more bullock carts, and the pandemonium appeared, if anything, to be worse.

I came to the crossing that leads into Jhaveri Bazaar, the market of jewellers. What a crowd of people: jabbering, rushing, pushing, smoking, eating. A cow was urinating in the road which was strewn with empty cigarette cartons and banana and orange skins and generously streaked with the blood-red juice spat out by pan addicts. A woman was crying for her child lost in the crowd; a few people seemed to be chasing a pickpocket. Thousands of people, men, women and children, beggars, sadhus, old men with sticks, young men in bush shirts, in dhotis and in pyjamas, all on the move, each on his own urgent business.

I wanted to try another temporary refuge and entered the first jeweller's shop which had a few customers and asked for a silver tumbler. The young man who attended asked: 'Hand-made or machine-turned? We have a wonderful collection.'

I selected one and asked the price. While the article was being weighed the man said: 'As an old customer (I had never been anywhere near the shop at any time) we will give you a discount of five per cent. We don't give it to others.'

'How is business?' I asked.

'Thanks to the reorganisation of the Sates I feel a stranger in my own city. We Gujratis have no future here.'

I held the tumbler and the packet of figs in my hand; the noise all around was so great, the stench so strong, that I wanted to get out quickly. I hailed a slow-moving taxi-cab and jumped into it. When, finally, we came out on to the main road the bearded Sikh driver started speaking to me.

'When the Gujratis have their own State, why shouldn't we Sikhs have our own? Damn these Congress-wallas!'

113

I

'You elected them', I pointed out.

'Elected!' he growled. 'They cannot be removed; too well dug in.'

That night, in the train going to Hyderabad, I thought of that mass of humanity, the milling crowd that every day throughout the years moved in the area of the Jhaveri Bazaar and elsewhere, of the eight million added every year to the 440 million swamping the land whose population was outgrowing food production.

Hyderabad was a city I knew well, its glitter and its gloom, the ornate palaces of the rich and the mud shanties of the poor. So saturated was this city with the past that however far back the mind roamed, it was impossible to detach oneself from its human background. I had roamed its streets and lanes and knew every monument and landmark. I had been connected with almost every one of the events that marked its last years, the death agonies of a culture and way of life which we loved and which was so unique, so urbane, the last vestiges of the courts of Akbar and Shah Jehan, the over-ripe fruit of the trees out of which had grown the glory of the Taj Mahal and the melodies of Tansen. Coming back after an absence of years to the city where I had lived and grown up gave me a strange, joyous feeling. But many things had changed; landmarks had disappeared, open spaces had been thoughtlessly built upon; new shops, coffee houses, eating places, had sprung up like mushrooms. The whole place was so full of people, so full of a lazy bustle. There were more cars, rickshaws, beggars and bicycles in the streets than I had ever seen before. The old atmosphere had vanished and the tempo of life had changed. The city seemed to have lost its character and the people their individuality. There was an air of commercialisation, a great deal of clamour, and yet there appeared no real joy or contentment in the faces of the people.

The past floated listlessly before my eyes. I was stricken by a strong nostalgia. Memories were crowding into my mind: our home, our many relatives, my school and college, the friends dead or forgotten. My own world of friends had almost perished. There was something like a magic dream clinging to everything I saw, yet deep down in my heart there was a feeling of being an alien in my own home.

I wanted to visit as many relatives, friends and acquaintances as possible in the four short days. Uncle Mumtaz was dead, so was Asif, and so were many others. Hyder was away somewhere in the North decorating a well-paid Government post.

Vasanth Rao, the clever advocate and agitator, who had once saved Rihaz from the jungle chief, Mallaraju, was now a cabinet minister and when I telephoned him he came over to take me to his home. I was touched by the warmth of his greetings. He had all the graces of a gentleman and knew the days when culture and good breeding counted in a man's daily life. Alas! they did not any longer. To him, power and status were ephemeral and he was not swept off his feet by the accident of success. We talked of the struggle of the days gone by, of the problems facing the country and his own hopes and disappointments. Vasanth Rao, I understood, was unpopular with his colleagues because of his radical views. He himself was critical and dissatisfied with the way things were going. Indeed, he admitted that he was disgusted with the unashamed fight for power and position among the many groups and cliques within the party, and had often thought of resignation.

'But the trouble is', he confessed, 'no effective opposition is possible, for there is no effective public opinion; once you cease to be a minister you are lost in the wilderness for ever.'

Vasanth Rao was so full of ideas and so eager to talk that I did not mind his excited monologues. I asked him about community development, land reforms and the Panchayat Raj, about which I had read so many interesting reports.

'Interesting reports? Yes, we are rather good at producing them', he said. 'We have a whole band of officials at headquarters who do nothing but produce reports. Rather good, aren't they?' he said sarcastically. Then, leaning over towards me, added: 'You tell me, how can we solve our gigantic problems by merely nibbling at them, how many of us really understand that progress calls for a fundamental structural change of society? It's no use talking about the awakening of the people. All this "destination man" stuff is just a masquerade. Has it really inspired people with confidence that they may change their lives by self-help? Has it tapped the springs of initiative choked for so long? No, nothing of this kind has happened. Our community development is a pretentious house without a foundation. What has it done beyond providing the villages, and mark you, not all of them, with just a few basic facilities? It has not generated enough capital to insure its future growth. Where is the nation-wide adjustment between agriculture and industry, between land and labour, between food and population? Where is the discipline and unity of aim and action needed to achieve success? You need an ideology and its relentless pursuit. At the moment we are only deluding ourselves with slogans.'

He paused for breath and I was lost in the torrent of his words.

'Yes, you asked me about land reform and Panchayats too. Well, by our half-hearted and isolated efforts we have only created a multitude of stagnating farms. It would be ridiculous to imagine that our legislators would want to commit suicide by reversing the present system of land-holding.'

'Have you in mind a system of collectives or co-operatives?' I interrupted.

'Why not?' he shot back. 'Call them collectives or co-operatives, if you wish, but it is only large-scale farming and improved agricultural techniques that can raise the level of productivity. But these collectives or co-operatives will not come by sermonising and pious resolutions. They require an honest and vigorous leadership.

'Panchayat Raj', he continued and there was a light of conviction in his eyes, 'is good if and when it works. I hope it will, one day. At the moment, however, we have only managed to carry our quarrels at the top down into the village houses, where nobody understands anything else. If we are to succeed, in fact, if we are to survive, we need an economy planned and controlled from the centre and not a hotch-potch of jerry-building.'

Meekly I remarked: 'However disappointed you may personally feel, one cannot fail to see, and I have done so in this short time, the great strides our country has made within her democratic forms and freedoms. There is bound to be some pressure of passions and politics if you believe in a government by popular consent.'

He rose from his chair to pick up a cigarette, then quietly said: 'I don't see how democracy gets compromised if people are made to work for their own good. However, I am a man in a hurry. If we don't catch up we'll be swallowed.'

On our way back home we called on Roop Karan, a mutual friend, who was once a university professor and now lived in retirement. Over a hurried cup of coffee he said: 'We had our ghair mulkies, our carpet-baggers, in the past; people who came for fat juicy jobs; but there is now the greatest migration of sharks in living memory. These are rustics and their hands still stink of manure. We are fed up with their petty-mindedness, their obscure intrigues, their greed and avarice. What annoys me most is that they cheat in the certainty of exercising a right.'

'Your annoyance, my dear Roop, is not going to help you', Vasanth Rao abruptly intervened. 'You have always been a nationalist by conviction; why don't you run for elections, Roop, you might be a minister?'

'Ah', he said, 'you want me to be a leader? I am no good for that. I have no illusions, I have no faculty for self-deception. That is for men like some of your colleagues who can blend their obvious personal interests with vague public ideals.'

In the evening I paid a visit to an old friend, Hari Narayen Prasad. We all called him Raja. He lived on the eastern side of the city, beyond the river, in his sprawling ancestral mansion, his devdi, part of which was now rented out. Raja and I had been colleagues in service and were, at one time, posted to a remote District. His people and mine had known each other for generations and we had come to regard ourselves as one family.

Unlike most aristocrats, Raja had chosen Government service as a career, had prepared himself for it and proved to be a capable officer. He was a connoisseur of good food and good living. He enjoyed entertaining and during festive seasons and ceremonial functions, of which there were many, his house overflowed with relatives and friends. When, however, in the wake of political change, the so-called reorganisation of the services took place, Raja was retired prematurely by the questionable use of a new ordinance. He had four daughters and five sons, and with his meagre retirement benefits and the reduced income from his jagir (estate) he found himself in financial straits.

He received me with open arms and tears in his eyes, moved by memories of the happy days we had spent together— memories of his devoted wife who was no more, of his young son-in-law who had suddenly died and of the many friends who were either dead or, because of reduced circumstances, preferred to stay at home. His sons and daughters were all there to welcome me, and it was a touching family reunion.

After a while, when they had left, Raja spoke of his immediate troubles : 'My main worry is to get Shakuntala and Parvati married and to get Narindar and Arjun fixed in Government service or a good business house. Nowadays it is very difficult to find decent young men for the girls. Those who are reasonably settled in life ask for enormous dowries which I can't afford. My boys are well qualified, but try as they may, they can't get a job. The outsiders have left us nowhere, really nowhere.'

My heart went out to this old aristocrat overwhelmed by the flood of new circumstances.

'We never thought of the future', he said, 'we lived only for the day. And that has brought us to this fate. Look at the new brood of Government officials; how wise they are! Many of them are real estate agents, doing a roaring business in land and property. If only I had had such forethought', he said with a touch of sarcasm, 'I should not be facing this plight.'

I asked him about some of our old friends.

'Friends', he said with sadness in his eyes. 'I have none. The true ones are either dead or never leave their homes. The others, well, when you can no longer dispense favours and have no money, have no more use for you. Human nature itself has changed, like everything else.' Then in a whisper charged with emotion he added: 'Even some of my own relatives have forsaken me. You wouldn't believe it, my own nephews do not bother to see me now.'

'Raja', I said, trying to console him, 'let us be brave and face facts. Times have changed and are changing everywhere. But to lament will take us nowhere and bitterness won't solve anything. You must pull yourself out of this mood of brooding, meet people again as you used to do and get a breath of fresh air, or you'll break up.'

'Fresh air! Where is it? I never go out of this house and perhaps never will. The new men of this generation are vandals, with no manners and no culture. They are rude and insulting and I would rather finish my time with whatever self-respect I have managed to save.'

Raja's family had now rejoined us and everybody insisted that I stayed for dinner. The women took over the conversation. We talked about the price of rice, dhal, vegetables, meat, eggs, milk and fuel, which had soared nearly five-fold; the difficulties of getting domestic servants and the exorbitant pay they were demanding. The girls were telling me how all the children in the schools had now to learn at least three languages: the national, the regional and a foreign language. While Narindar recited a list of high-sounding and almost unpronounceable Hindi words which had replaced well-known Urdu or English equivalents, Arjun made us laugh with a story about a Minister who at the end of a formal dinner loudly licked curds off his fingers and washed his false teeth in the finger-bowl.

After a delightful meal I started homeward through the deserted lanes of the old city, poorly lit and dusty, flanked on either side by block upon block of jagged houses and crumbling devdis, the palaces of yesterday. I knew some of these were the guardians of history but their unlighted windows tonight were like the empty sockets of eyes which had seen much of secret crime and dark intrigue. Here and there a few pan and bidi shops were open, some people were fast asleep on the pavements, some were hawking rotten vegetables and bananas, an old woman was yawning as she waited patiently under a flickering kerosene lamp to sell tiny bundles of twigs for fuel, stray donkeys were standing silently near the over-filled dustbins and a few frightened cats hurriedly crossed the road. Men with turbans and veiled women in long black garments were seen begging from door to door. Those bye-lanes seemed to speak to me in a sad bitter language compounded of human misery, frustration, squalor and gloom. I knew some of the people who once lived in those houses and devdis; some of them might still be there inside those grey and dilapidated walls, huddled together, I had no doubt, with cockroaches and bugs. My chauffeur, son of a once well-to-do father, told me that some of those asking for alms and food were not so very long ago themselves the donors of charity but now came out to beg at night to avoid recognition.

Driving slowly, we came on to a large square teeming with people just out of the nearby cinemas, all jabbering and all in a hurry. According to my chauffeur, the only places at which people now gathered in large numbers were either the cinemas, where the young and not-so-young thronged to see the long-drawn-out movies and clapped and whistled in appreciation, or the sendhikhanas,* where the poor went after the day's toil to drown their cares and sorrows, or the Darghas, the tombs of saints, where the old and the middle-aged assembled to pray for better times or an honourable deliverance from their miseries.

'Of course,' he added, 'there are any number of those new eating places where coffee, tea, pakodas, wadas and other snacks are served for those who can afford them.'

The rest of my time in Hyderabad was spent in paying brief visits to scores of relatives and friends, as many of them as I could possibly manage to see.

Boma was an old, semi-paralysed, widowed friend of the family. She was a grand character, God-fearing and full of affection. She always had a kind word for everybody and offered prayers for them all. She had two grown-up daughters and a son. The elder daughter, Rohaina, had been married to a Sindhi in Pakistan but returned home within weeks of the wedding when she discovered that the man not only had another wife but also a mistress by whom he had a child. The ill-tempered man had deceived her parents with falsehoods about his income and property.

* Local open-air taverns selling the fermented juice of sendhi or toddy trees.

Immediately after the events of 1948, Boma's son had left for Pakistan on an impulse, without even telling his mother, in the hope of finding a living. Poor Aunty Boma, now left alone with her two daughters, longed to have her son back but, alas! tears and prayers did not help; he had obtained the citizenship of that country although not the kind of job he had expected. This proud woman was trying to run the household single-handed (almost from her bed) on an income of three hundred rupees which she received as rent from the block of flats she owned in the city. She was obviously selling her family jewellery to make ends meet.

'You have come back, baita (my son)', said Aunty Boma, blessing me with a long prayer, holding my bowed head in both her hands. She was soon crying piteously for her self-exiled son.

'My days in the world are few, I want to have my Khalid with me before I die. He was foolish to have gone away and I know he is eager to come back but I hear that there are laws which do not permit this. May Allah give the authorities the wisdom and mercy to help a dying woman.'

Talking about her two daughters, Boma said: 'You have perhaps heard about Rohaina. What a tragic business! I don't know what to do with her. Who would marry her now? Divorce proceedings in a foreign country are not easy. She now spends four whole days a week in the Women's Club, gambling at what they call rummy or something, and keeps herself busy with dozens of her women friends in endless gossip. Thank Allah, your uncle's eyes were closed before this happened, but what can I do?'

And she continued, vaguely looking at me with her dim, sorrowful eyes: 'Hers is not a good example, too, for poor Jehanaara. She is a nice girl, just graduated, but I can't find a match for her.'

She added after a pause: 'Jehanaara has just started helping in the women's college library; I know your uncle would not have approved, but that is the best that could have happened in the circumstances.'

Bijani was a distant cousin of ours and was married to a man who had worked in one of the many secretariats at Headquarters. His life was centred around the family and the routine duties of his office; he had no outside interests and no hobbies. He had very rarely left the municipal limits of the city and when, therefore, as a result of the State's reorganisation he was transferred to a touring job in a remote and far-off place in another State, his troubles began.

Bijani was very happy to see me.

'May Allah keep you well, bawa (son). I knew you would turn up one day to help us in our plight; you alone can do it and no one else', she said in a voice quivering with hope.

'What is the matter?' I asked, somewhat embarrassed and wondering if I could measure up to the faith she reposed in me.

'He* has been transferred to Maharashtra; he was so simple and so honest that he did not know whom to approach and how, and he was packed off, and here I am left without him with the five children to look after.'

'Why don't you all go and live with him?' I replied.

'Please give a thought to my reasons, bawa', she said imploringly. 'My children are well advanced in their Telugu and only Marathi is taught in the place he has been transferred to, and it has no high school either. Then, we pay no rent for this house for we live with his old father; we can neither take the old man with us nor leave him here', she continued. 'Fifteen days in a month he wanders about from village to village where people speak a different tongue. He has to keep a house for himself and yet he sends us more than two-thirds of his monthly salary and that is not enough to run this house, pay for the schooling of the children, their clothes, books and their transport to the schools. The poor children, you must see them, they are growing up well. I have not been able to give them new clothes for the last two 'Ids.† Help me by getting him sent back here.'

I was sad at being unable to help her and at her look of disappointment, but it was a matter in which I was helpless.

I met Koti Venkata Reddi in the Friends Club one evening, a man in his sixties, thin, with rather a longish face and under his eyes were deep smudges of black which seemed violet in the harsh light of the club lounge. He had once been a school teacher in Puloor and had now moved to Hyderabad to make it his permanent home. He told me that some of his acquaintances had done so earlier with profit, and had made money; first by clever trading in real estate, then by building and sale of property. He himself had some plans in this direction and hoped soon to acquire a house; maybe, in the not too distant future, he would even own an hotel. A man had to be satisfied with that these days. The rotten riches of the old aristocrats belonged to the past. To

* Wives always referred to their husbands as 'he' and never by name.
† 'Id is a Muslim festival when the children are traditionally provided with new clothes.

121

emulate them was beyond the realm of possibility. I could almost feel the envy in his voice.

'The people of Hyderabad never made use of their opportunities and now they blame us for exploiting them', he said, drawing up his bare feet and thin naked legs on to the chair. 'What I so dislike in them is their pride. They consider themselves the salt of the earth and expect that their so-called culture and their exalted past entitles them to a grand funeral. This we'll not concede. Their culture, based upon exploitation, was confined to a few hundred families in the cities only, mind you, and so fragile was it that it was shattered at the first impact of change. What was their past, may I ask? Historically: naked conquest and holding on to power, the purpose of which was nothing but idleness and a life of ease.'

Venkata Reddi licked his lips and stubbed out his cigarette on the cement floor and continued: 'I do not like them, for there is no limit to their vanity. They think that the civilised way is theirs alone and all the oddities are ours. We may not have their ways, I admit, we can't perhaps use tables and chairs as they do, but does that mean anything?' He was talking loudly now, belching intermittently and arranging and rearranging his scanty dhoti. 'What do they want: sleep, perhaps? They are all frozen in the past.' And then he said after a brief pause: 'They hate anyone who tries to wake them or even behave differently.'

'The behaviour of these old families is vitally connected with their heritage of memories', I said. 'People with different ways of living whom they call upstarts or outsiders merely upset their illusions of acquired perfection. Why not give them the funeral they deserve?'

That day I also met various other friends: a once fashionable officer, now bearded and religious; an old official who remarried a young girl and was at odds with his grown-up sons; a bunch of prematurely retired colleagues and sons of ex-Jagirdars who did nothing else but spend their days playing cards; a widowed Begum complaining about her sons' squandering what remained of the ancestral fortune on horses, dogs and drink; a young doctor with a successful practice who had devoted his life to his people; a once flourishing shopkeeper who told me he was closing down because the newcomers did not care for the fashionable wares he sold.

Before going out to dinner that night in the city, I dropped in at my old, exclusive club. Membership was now open to everyone who could afford the high subscription and prices. As a result, the new society of business men, contractors, shopkeepers and others had become its members and many were there in the early evening. The old habits of dress and decorum had vanished. Some were in bush shirts and shorts, some in trousers and open-necked shirts, others in dhotis and slippers; and amidst shouts for drinks and loud talk and laughter, club servants, 'boys' in white (and not so white) uniform, were hurriedly arranging chairs and tables for the bi-weekly session of Bingo, a game of chance that the newly emancipated women particularly liked.

What a change! But typical, perhaps, of the difference between the new and the old.

Jhango Nawab knew that the wealth he had inherited from his ancestors had provided him all these years with a carefree and leisurely life. But now that political change had reached his own threshold and the new Government had confiscated his Jagir, granting him a meagre long-term compensation, he was shocked to find that the wealth he had taken for granted had become the cause of all his troubles. His brothers and sisters, legitimate or otherwise, and a host of other relatives had dragged him into expensive litigation, demanding their share in the income and property which had long been denied them by the feudal hierarchy and the special regulations for Crown Grants. Then his eldest son, the apple of his eye, had left the shelter of his father's roof and applied to a Civil Court for a division of the family property. The Nawab had always been opposed to the idea of his dear Badai Nawab, his eldest son, marrying into a class which was not his own and into a family too modern for his taste. And now his worst foreboding had come true: it was his son's father-in-law who was behind this outrageous lawsuit.

The Nawab's shrunken income had compelled him to reduce the eight courses of his dinner to three; the number of his cars and servants had similarly dwindled. He now had to apply to some wretched understrapper even for permission to go shooting, and ammunition was both expensive and difficult to obtain. How could he stoop to beg for permits to shoot his tigers and restrict himself to areas not of his own choice? After all, he had a position to maintain!

I had known Jhango Nawab rather well. In common with some others of his class he had little claim to brains and no pretensions to education. He had grown up in the company of illiterate male servants and doting old women. Being the heir presumptive, he had, even before the death of his father, everything and everybody at his beck and call.

Still he had a dignity and a code to which he continued to be true. In his youth he was a dashing young man, full of life, somewhat erratic and emotional. Amidst the fun and frolic of his shikar parties, the excursions to his Jagir and his busy social life, he lived happily in his own way, yet he lived in the past, drawing upon the glories of his ancestors. He had a store of anecdotes, many of them the product of fancy, about his fore-fathers: how, for instance, his illustrious Badai Dada Jan (his great-great-grandfather) had saved his monarch's life by chopping off the trunk of a charging elephant with a single stroke of that famous sword of Isphahan, said to be a gift from the Shah of Persia to one of his ancestors ('I now have that sword in my armoury'); and how, even fifty years ago, his uncle, who was a wonderful marksman, could bring down a flying duck by shoot-ing it through its right eye! He could relate for hours to his friends and others stories of harems and horses, of Meh-Jabeens* and motorcars. Yet he had something of the simplicity of a child and his vitriolic temper was matched by an equal gener-osity.

The scores of servants, including family jesters, who had grown up with him and catered to his ego through flattery, were the first to be hit by his misfortune. The usual large supply of rice, ghee (clarified butter) and goats from his steward, the Naib of the Jagir, had ceased and the once free and abundant feeding at the devdi had been considerably reduced. They knew that everything was no longer at rights with their master. The six men who took turns of two hours each to massage his legs when he slept were told that he could afford only two. What greater tragedy could have befallen the proud Nawab when he had to dispense with his life-long companions, companions with whom he had hunted, shared confidences and discussed daily gossip? Alas, the very sustainers of his morale and the builders of his ego had to leave him.

Driving over to the Nawab's enormous ancestral palace in Mahboob ki Mehndi, it pained me to see its dilapidated condi-tion; the gleaming white-washed attics over the imposing entrance arch, where drums and pipes were played daily at set hours, were now black with soot and empty; the rooms below, which housed his bodyguard, were now rented out to a shop selling tea and pan (betel) which catered to the hundreds of peons and petty clerks of the various offices that were now accommodated in the palace itself.

I remembered the palace at the time of Jhango Nawab's wedding some twenty-five years ago, and it seemed but yesterday.

* Pretty girls.

Not a labourer, mason or electrician was available to the other people in the city for weeks together, so lavish were the preparations and so extensive the entertainments. Jhango Nawab enjoyed being the centre of all that pomp and splendour. He had confided to me, I recollected, that he had not even stopped to wonder what his bride would be like; his grandmother had assured him that she was young, beautiful and healthy and was bringing a big dowry. What more could he ask for? Education for women was not in keeping with the family traditions; in fact, it was a disqualification. She had only learned to read the Quran which she religiously recited every Friday.

And what a wedding it was! His family would omit not even one item of custom or ceremony: each rite starting late in the evening, went on far into the early hours of the morning; and this continued for weeks together. With scores of slave girls of all ages—some old and infirm whom he had inherited from his father and grandfather; some still young and once pretty, who had been his favourites in early youth—there was never a shortage of help for the endless work involved in performing the ceremonies and in feeding the numerous guests, day in and day out.

Before the actual wedding the groom's mother inspected the bride's right instep to make sure that the light could pass underneath it: a certain sign that she would bring good luck to the home she stepped into. Then her foot had to be measured for the bridal shoes; this was done by the bride's sister who would stretch a string of pearls from the heel to the toe, and woe betide the bride if the pearls did not count up to an even number. But with a knowing sister this was always possible!

I remember sharing Jhango Nawab's sudden nervousness when he was preparing for the first glimpse of the bride. The religious ceremony was over and they were seated on the bridal dais surrounded by a milling crowd of guests. A silver-framed mirror was held under the face of the bride, whose head was bent very low, and it was in the reflection that she and the groom exchanged their first glimpse of each other. Gently he parted the strands of jasmine that covered her face, but all that he could see was the bejewelled nose-ring and the gold-dust sparkling upon her eyelids. It was only when he lifted her after the Nikha* from the bedecked throne to carry her to the car in which they were to drive home that he knew she was slim and lissom. Entering the bridal chamber, he thought that the ceremonies were over, but his special maid-servant, who had brought him up as a child, reminded him that he had to pray on part of the crimson

* The final ceremony indicating acceptance and registration.

cloth that had covered his bride as an offering of gratitude to the Almighty; that he also had to feed the bride with sweet rice, kheer, placed on a silver coin (making certain that only the kheer was eaten!). This, as an undertaking that he would be responsible for her protection and welfare; and then to wash her feet with milk, as a token of his submission. All this done, he was left to himself at last to have a proper look for the first time at the woman who was to be his life-long companion.

I remember, too, Jhango Nawab telling me that when he hurriedly uncovered her head and parted the Sehra of flowers and gold tinsel, lifting the face which from modesty she struggled to avert, he had thought that she could have been a little fairer and her nostrils less prominent. To Jhango the eyes were very important and I could recall his telling me how he had pleaded with her to open them, but then the bride remembered her own mother's repeated parting warnings that on no account was she to open her eyes or utter a word in his presence for three whole days.

Whatever his failings—and they were many—however blind and unconcerned he was to reality, the Nawab was now a shattered man. Gone was the gaiety and the fun. How long could he live by selling and mortgaging ancestral property, how long could he endure the relentless, day-to-day pestering by creditors and lawyers, how long could he bear the daily insults and humiliations? Had he not taken large loans, at fancy rates of interest, four years ago, for the magnificent wedding of his now ungrateful son? Had he not tried to keep up appearances by retaining two cars, by maintaining a horde of servants, by observing in a fitting manner all traditional feasts and holy days, even though all this meant secretly selling his wife's jewellery?

The world around Jhango Nawab had violently erupted and changed: and the change had come so suddenly, like a bolt from the blue. He had thought that his was an unchanging world. Was not his State the State Eternal, Sulthanath-i-abdmudat, and was not his ruler the Shadow of God, Zel-o-subhani?

Nobody knew or cared today what importance he had enjoyed in the past and what illustrious part his long line of ancestors had played in the life of the State and society, the society which was at present witnessing his downfall and ruin. It was not so much the loss of wealth that mattered to him as the loss of faith in the life in which he had been brought up.

It was not long before the final blow struck him. Even the meagre compensation for his Jagir, which he received in half-yearly instalments, was withheld by an injunction of the Civil

Court. His cars were sold in partial payment of his debts, his antique furniture, the Venetian chandeliers and the Mappin & Webb silverware which his grandfather had received as a gift from the Prime Minister, were auctioned. His sons, already in bad company, had taken to heavy drinking and gambling, and it was whispered to him that one of his daughters, failing to elope with the son of a shopkeeper, had tried to commit suicide.

One day, when he went to his old club to resign his membership, as he could no longer afford to pay even its modest subscription, he was told by a friend that the night before his daughter-in-law had danced in the club until the late hours of the morning. How could he bear that indignity? The cup of misery had overflowed. Asking for God's mercy, he returned straight to his wife. In the days of adversity she was the only person who, within her own limitations, had tried to console and comfort him. She did not know what had befallen her husband when he entered the house and broke down sobbing on her shoulder, something which he had never done before. Thinking that the summons of the Civil Court served on him might have upset him, she rushed into her room and brought the remnants of the jewellery given her by her mother and laid them at his feet.

'My Sardar, my Sahib, may my life be sacrificed for you; you can sell this, sell everything I have', she said imploringly with a flood of tears.

'May Allah have mercy on us. Begum, it is the humiliation and dishonour that has been brought to the family's name. It is now in the dust. Imagine', he blubbered, his voice choked with emotion, 'my daughter-in-law, the granddaughter-in-law of Himmat-ul-Mulk, dancing before everybody, in the arms of these new bastards!'

She tried to soothe him. 'It may be the wagging of malicious tongues. It may be she has danced only with her husband. Times have changed, Sahib', she pleaded, 'we are back numbers; we live in a past that is long dead. ... Don't you know the daughter of Nawab Viqar and the wife of Nawab Akbar dance, too? Let them live as they please, forget it!'

'Forget it! How can I?' Jhango cried in anguish. Choking, his face all swollen, he had to be carried to his bed, where a few days later he died.

Jhango Nawab, the last of the line of Iftikar-ud-Daulah, the great soldier of fortune who had triumphantly entered the city with the conqueror, the founder of the ruling dynasty nearly two hundred years ago, died of a stroke of rage and a broken heart. His family and his host of cooks, chambermaids, slave girls and servants who had been with him to the end would soon be on the merciless streets of the city.

I went to see another old acquaintance of mine, Kabir Arsalan. He was in his late sixties, round face, large bald head, thin grey hair on the sides, thoughtful dark eyes, a perfect set of original teeth and thick black eyebrows. He had obviously withstood well the encroachments of time. His movements were free and mind alert. He was a confirmed bachelor, but often talked with relish about the numerous rich spinsters who had tried to lure him into matrimony. Educated at Oxford and widely travelled, he always considered himself an intellectual. On retirement from the Civil Service, although he confined himself to his modern house and its extensive grounds, he busied himself in enlarging his domain by ways, many people thought, not in keeping with his intellectual pose. Whatever the merits of the various accusations, his character, complex and unfathomable, intrigued even the closest of his friends. Yet he had an old-fashioned manner, unhurried and graceful.

We talked about the generation of people which was fast disappearing.

'Ah, I can think of only a few hundred persons who make up that generation today. You often meet them, almost all of them, at weddings and funerals. They are never tired of exchanging compliments and mutual congratulations, always with circumscribed politeness', he said, wiping the sweat from his brows with his coloured handkerchief. Then gazing at me somewhat gloomily, he continued: 'These people are struggling to keep up appearances, clinging to life for life's own sake. They are mere shadows, moving, perhaps, in freedom, but having nowhere to go. . . .'

I broke in: 'How do you feel yourself?'

'I', he said with a faint trace of irritation, 'I feel free and chained at the same time, as one feels just before the polling day, when all the crooks have been nominated and you are beseeched to vote for the right man!'

Kabir Arsalan was in a critical mood, and I encouraged him. He went on: 'It would have been no tragedy if these people of the shadows were genuinely poor like so many others but the trouble is that they still live mentally in a world where they could afford to be lavish with money.'

Talking about other countries I told him of how our own is associated abroad with high moral principles and how our survival may depend upon living up to them.

His eyes gleamed. Giving me a rare and mischievous smile, he said: 'It is nice to talk about honour, our spiritual heritage, past glory, tolerance, Gandhi and all that, but...' he added as if he was hesitating to say it, 'principles are all right so long as we do not put them into practice.'

I did enjoy the long talk with Kabir Arsalan but could not avoid a vague suspicion that, as usual, he was quoting from some book.

Late that night, on the first part of my journey to Venkatapur, in the loneliness of that dusty railway compartment, I went over the events of the past four days and the people I had met. Most of these people were, by and large, contemporaries of Rihaz and were part of a society which had been caught unprepared by the blast of changes that had destroyed overnight the pattern of their lives. On the canvas of time these changes appear unimportant; but for the people concerned they were like a whirlwind, making no distinction between the guilty and the innocent, between the farseeing and the foolish. With impartial violence, it had destroyed their world at one stroke.

Now I found in them neither the capacity nor the wish to strive; their minds and bodies had ceased to function. There was everywhere apathy and depression, resignation and frustration. Even in their dumb acquiescence, in their ever-present despair and pessimism I heard complaints about discrimination and injustice and protests against a world which, in their thinking, had suddenly been caught up in the grip of dishonesty, intrigue, hypocrisy, and greed, in which there was no glimmer of hope or fair play. Doubtless, here was a society stagnant and disintegrating towards its inevitable doom. For these people, who were no more than pawns in the hands of history, tomorrow did not exist, today was a horrible reality and only the dead yesterday mattered.

It would take a long time, perhaps, another decade or two, for this generation of men and women, still bewildered and shocked, to vanish and a new one to take its place, one which would adapt and adjust itself to the merciless changes that time had wrought.

Early the next morning our train arrived at a wayside station, from where we were to proceed by bullock-cart to Venkatapur. I was met by two enthusiastic young men, Luxman, the Block Development Officer, and Anand, the Village Level Worker, the new category of functionaries who were engaged in rural develop-

129

K

ment. As we jolted along the dusty road, the stars were still gleaming in the dark sky and the air was fresh, cool and crisp. Except for the rattle of the cart and the merry tinkle of the little bells around the bullocks' necks, quiet and peace prevailed. Soon the darkness began to grow limpid and the fields on both sides of the road were now bathed in a soft light and we could see the mellow haze on the trees and meadows. Although it was difficult to carry on sustained conversation, Anand, who was driving the cart, bombarded me with questions about life abroad, while I was trying to ask him about old friends in Venkatapur. He was an energetic, alert young man, just a year out of his training school.

As we were nearing the outskirts of the village I was excited to see the pinnacle of the old temple, tinted with the glow of the rising sun, standing out against the pale blue sky. I was lost in reverie, gazing at the once familiar landmark and at the open fields with their unbounded horizons, until I heard the fond address of Pulliah's son who had come out along with a few friends to meet me. They had brought for me coconuts and garlands of yellow marigold, the traditional offerings of welcome.

I got off the cart and while we walked towards the village there were affectionate greetings and inquiries about Rihaz. The village was waking up as we entered: smoke wisps were curling out of a few huts; some people puffing bidis were either coming from or going to the nearby fields where they eased themselves; cattle were being led out of the houses by small boys in torn clothes; women in colourful saris were drawing water from the well; some were scrubbing their pots and pans; under the pipal tree a few persons were leisurely chatting and cleaning their teeth with fresh neem twigs; the half-clad Pujari, with his shining head, except for a tiny tuft of hair left unshaved on the crown, was solemnly chanting 'Mantras' in the temple yard while sprinkling holy water over some fading flowers, betel leaves and coconuts. While this picture awakened in me the memories of the past, I felt that, except for a few new buildings like the school, the Community Hall, the clinic, and some privately built clean new huts, Venkatapur had remained much the same as pictured by Rihaz, and as I myself had seen it years ago. Of course, there were new faces, a whole generation of them. To many of these, Rihaz must have been just a memory of a name of whom their fathers had tenderly spoken.

I strolled in the village and chatted with the people. Many were the sons of friends Rihaz had described; and some, particularly the outcast Dheds, actually knew that the village owed the beginnings of its good fortune to the man whose friend was now visiting them.

We were passing Saiga's hut. Among the Harijans in the neighbouring communities, he was one of the two whose sons had matriculated. Having known him years ago, I stopped. Hearing unfamiliar voices, he hurried out, bent almost double as he stooped through the low opening of his thatched mud hut, wiping his hands with what remained of his time-worn dhoti. The broad toothless grin which clung to his thin, weather-beaten face and the humble salutation of the joined palms showed his recognition and welcome.

'How are you, Saiga? Do you remember me? And how are those two sons of yours?'

'How could I forget you, sir?' he answered a little reproachfully. 'You used to come with Rihaz Durra, I remember so well. How is he? My sons work in the town; one is a clerk in the Tehsil office and the other works in the new mill.'

As was customary, he invited me into his hut. At the entrance stood a largish earthenware jar, securely sealed with mud and straw, containing his year's meagre savings of jawar. Saiga's wife was pounding chillies with a wooden pestle in a stone mortar, half sunk into the floor. She withdrew quickly into a corner, covering her head with the end of her sari. A very old woman with untidy hair and a sickly look sat nearby. She was Saiga's mother. The mud floor of the hut had been freshly sprinkled with a mixture of cow dung and red earth; there was no furniture of any kind, not even a cot. The earthenware pots and pans were neatly arranged in one corner; a few clothes hung on a cord that was stretched across the hut. The cow-dung fire was smouldering in the cooking place, the chula, and immediately above, hanging from the ceiling, were two bottles of oil. Nearby stood a pot of fresh milk, with a small cloud of flies buzzing over it.

'Our buffalo calved four days ago', said Saiga proudly.

I could see the buffalo, and even smell her, in the small back yard, leisurely switching her tail to drive the flies from her emaciated flanks. They rose, only to settle on her again. The newly born calf was occupying a corner of the hut screened off by dried jawar stalks tied together. The family bedding, a crude black blanket, a straw mat and an improvised pillow, was thrown over a bush outside to dry. A few chickens were searching for worms in a nearby rubbish dump.

'Wouldn't you have preferred your sons to stay here with you? They would have been such a help?' I remarked.

'You know, Durra, how it is with the boys today. They think it beneath their dignity to work in the fields. They rarely come to see me but I am glad they have good positions and earn a decent wage.'

I could understand Saiga. His boys were the first in the community to read and write and had, therefore, acquired a higher social status and he was proudly conscious of this fact.

'Saiga, you could earn much more, I think, if you had another buffalo and a few more hens; then, perhaps, you could have a better hut.'

'That would mean, Durra, that I am ungrateful to God and not satisfied with what He has given me—I have enough.'

And this was a man living on the very edge of subsistence!

Late that evening I visited Ramulu, the son of Pulliah, the money-lender, who some years ago had been hacked to death by the Communists. Being Banias by caste, money-lending was their hereditary profession, but after the father's murder the son, who had managed to retrieve some money and about forty acres of land, had taken to agriculture.

It was getting dark when I reached the house, a solid structure of stone and mud. It had been one of the few well-built houses in the village, but when the Communists set fire to most of the family property a large part of the house had burnt down and had been rebuilt only recently. The strong wooden door that barred the entrance remained unscathed and stood before me, solid as ever with its serried ranks of heavy nails to deter an intruder. Cattle returning from the fields had just passed by and the dust had not yet settled back upon the road. Ramulu opened the door himself and we entered a narrow passage flanked by clay platforms which were covered by straw mattresses. It was here that in the days gone by his father used to transact most of his business, in endless negotiations.

Inside it was almost dark. A small lamp was smoking against a deeply coloured wall to which were nailed a faded print of Luxmi, the Goddess of wealth, and an out-of-date commercial calendar. Just beyond was a stone paved courtyard, open to the stars, where the cattle had been tethered. I could hear the munching in the darkness and the stamping of feet. A veranda that served as a kind of living-room ran along the four sides, its massive roof supported by thick pillars.

In a far corner there was a slow-burning fire and nearby were a few brass utensils. One side of the quadrangle was half filled with a stack of maize; two huge dried pumpkins hung from the ceiling; mosquitoes came whirring in and the smell of cow dung pervaded the air.

We sat down on one of the platforms and Ramulu presented his other guest, Ramachander Rao, a young man who had come from the town nearby which was the District Headquarters. Ramachander Rao was the son of a Patwari, a law graduate and a practising advocate. He must have been in his late twenties or early thirties but had already gone bald. His crooked nose sat oddly upon his intelligent face. He was wearing a white khadder shirt and a thin cotton dhoti. Ramulu's old mother walked in out of the darkness, silent and barefooted. Her movements were slow and she shyly brought the usual betel leaves, coconuts and a few marigolds in a shining brass tray to welcome me. She was plump, wore no bangles. The end of her sari covered her head which had been shaved, as ordained for a widow. In the dim light of the lamp she looked at me with eyes that had no expression except a remote sadness and, after gently whispering a gracious and touching word of greeting, she bade her five-year-old granddaughter daub a little red vermilion paste on my forehead to signify that I had been welcomed into the house. As unobtrusively as she had come she retired into the darkness where the other women of the family would have gathered.

Ramachander was describing to me some of the improvements made in recent years. Electricity had been brought to the town; there was a piped water supply system, two new factories and an intermediate college, and the hospital had been extended.

'Yes', I said, 'I myself have seen something of this silent revolution everywhere.'

'I won't call it a revolution, sir', answered Ramachander with a touch of assurance. 'These are some of the amenities long denied to the people. In themselves they are an advance, but there is no collective action nor collective development. A revolution needs a collective change in attitudes and that can only come by changes in the social order.'

'Look', I said, 'at the new road, the school and the community centre built by the people of this village. Don't they show a change in attitudes?'

'Ah, these are the fruits of short-lived enthusiasm for limited projects; there is no revolution as such. The necessary climate and the mood are not there. Where is the heady madness for winning through? Inertia, poverty and injustices still remain with us, and we continue to exist unconcernedly.'

Ramulu, of course, did not understand very much of what was being said, but when I asked him what he thought about

133

the change, his reply was prompt. 'Well, a few of us perhaps are earning a little more today because of higher agricultural prices; then there is the new school, the clinic, fertilisers for those who can afford the price, loans for those who can provide surety; but the village remains much the same. Most of us are as poor as before and while there are many to whom we can take our troubles, there is none who can offer quick redress.'

In some dumb, remote fashion, he seemed to sense something missing. He did not know what it was. The old authority, aloof and respected, had been displaced, but the new order had not yet filled the void. To him it was difficult to understand how the 'boy from next door' could become a Cabinet Minister overnight and acquire the wisdom to take the right decisions. He was, after all, only one of themselves.

'Do you find a change in the attitude of Government officials?' I asked.

'In your day, sir, officers took immediate decisions, but nowadays no officer decides anything unless his clerk writes for him on the file.'

'And quotes an Order of the Governor-in-Council of 1868', Ramachander Rao broke in with a mischievous smile, and added after a pause, '.. this is besides his constant fear of getting a charge memo or a "show cause" notice.'

'Why don't you enter politics, Mr Rao?' I inquired.

He replied quietly: 'Politics and piety are two of our great curses.'

After dinner I sat down to a talk with the Block officials and listened to their reports, their difficulties, handicaps, hopes and fears. I could feel that the village leadership had undergone a change. The hereditary Patel and the Patwari were there but with much less power; the Bania was no longer the controller of the village destinies.

The Deshmukh's family now wielded a different kind of influence. His third son was an elected member of the State Legislative Assembly. The wily old Deshmukh, like all other big landowners, when he saw that Government was introducing land reforms, quickly divided his large estate amongst his three sons and other relatives so that each could have the maximum area permissible, which meant that the family retained all the lands they possessed, even after the introduction of land reforms.

The Deshmukh's second son, Narsing Rao, unlike the other two, was highly educated and had developed a social conscience, but he was perhaps not clever at manoeuvring things and was therefore unable to get a place on the political ladder. Although his younger brother had political power, Narsing Rao had quite an influence in the affairs of the village without even being a member of the Panchayat. He was well known for his charities and for his help and sympathy for the people, who respected him.

Late during the next evening I had a meeting with the members of the Panchayat. Four of the members and some others turned up, but only three of them could contribute to the discussions as the others, looking bewildered and perplexed, were merely nodding their heads.

Our discussions did not go with a swing. 'What is your budget?' I asked. Konda Reddi (who was from the ruling party and president of the Panchayat) replied: 'The Inspector Sahib will be able to explain to you all about it.'

'What are your aims?'

Konda Reddi: 'Power for the people. You see, I was not able to look into the face of the Collector; of course I was not president then. Now he greets me with Namaste. I can speak to the Minister himself. . . .'

Narayan (who belonged to the same party but to a dissident group): 'The aim is to have power, yes, but in whose hands I do not know.'

Rajeswar (who sat on the fence and seemed to act as mediator): 'Let us not quarrel in front of the distinguished visitor. Our aim is to help the people.'

'How are you helping the people?'

Konda Reddi: 'I have dug a long side-drain. Our school has three teachers now, a year ago we had only one. . . .'

Narayan, interrupting: 'It is our group who got the two new teachers.'

'What are your difficulties?'

Konda Reddi: 'Not many. The Patwari, I suppose, is our biggest headache. I administer all our grants, I buy stationery, I sanction contracts . . . people depend on me. . . .'

Narayan (who obviously had something to say about the contracts, but restrained himself after a quick glance at Rajeswar): 'The Public Works Department has not completed the work over the nala (drain) which they promised two years ago . . . neither medicines nor fertilisers ever arrive in time. . . .'

Konda Reddi: 'I have already spoken to the Collector and also to the Minister and they have promised to help.'

Narayan: 'When exactly did you speak to them? I have been hearing of this for more than a year now.'

Rajeswar: 'Yes, it has taken a long time, but we can write

to the Minister once again. I myself went twice to see the Collector and the Tehsildar, but they were busy with arrangements for some ministerial visits.'

'Could not your representative in the Assembly help you?'

Narayan: 'Oh, there are wheels within wheels and the Ministers, even if they belong to the same group, have to convince the big officials who alone know the files and the rules.'

I asked Yelliah, the depressed-class member of the Panchayat who had kept quiet all the time, if he had anything to say. Casting embarrassed glances towards Konda Reddi, he meekly said: 'The Collector Sahib is a good man. We Harijans now have a seat in the Panchayat. ... I remember the good old days. We have not forgotten you Durra. .. Can you get us some straw so that we can rethatch our huts?'

When we were just getting into the proudly displayed waiting Panchayat jeep (I had overheard something about false expenditure on petrol), Yelliah whispered to me: 'My gang of workers have not yet received their due for digging the side-drain.'

Narsing Rao was a young man in his late twenties. He wore thick glasses and had an intelligent face. After a brilliant career at the local university, where he took a first in economics, he and his younger brother tried to get into politics, but the latter was craftier and was elected as an MLA (Member of the Legislative Assembly) from the Venkatapur constituency. During our conversation, Narsing Rao tried to show that he attached no consequence to his failure, but inwardly he seemed to nurse a grievance, not so much against his brother as against the party bosses. He spent the greater part of the year in Venkatapur looking after his share of the property and, interested as he was in the welfare of the people, he helped them in many ways, although he apparently did not like the way things were moving.

We talked about the old days and his late father and he told me how much he owed to Rihaz because it was at Rihaz's insistence, he said, that his father had sent him to school and, later, to college.

'In a country which is underdeveloped and tries to achieve democracy in a leap, I sometimes feel that if you want to be a man of consequence you should either be a politician or a bully', he remarked at one stage of our talks, and added smilingly after a pause: 'I know it is hard to draw a line between the two, isn't it?'

'One has to make a beginning somewhere, sometime', I retorted. 'Look at your Panchayat, for instance. With all the ignorance and the feuds and perhaps a little corruption, there is

136

at least a flicker of a consciousness. People are slowly beginning to know their rights.'

'Quite so', he said drily. 'I wish they also knew their obligations. I don't say it is wrong to indulge in democratic experiments, but look how we are doing it. Who are these members of the Panchayat? Do they represent anyone but themselves, anything but their own enmities and ambitions? Is talent really recognised in this country? You have only to catch the eye of the party boss, follow the party line, make as much noise as you can and you're well on the way up the ladder.' After some moments of hesitation, he added in a voice which betrayed disappointment, 'If there is a man who dared to say all that he thought of the present state of affairs, there would not be left him a square foot of ground to stand on. . . .'

'What about the Bhoodan movement?' I asked.

'My younger brother, the MLA, announced the gift of a hundred acres of land when Vinobaji* was here. But how many people know that the land in question had been for years a subject of litigation and my brother has the weakest possible claims to it? Our president of the Panchayat announced two "magnificent gifts" on his own behalf: one was a piece of land he had sold years ago, and the other was a rocky plot of no use to anybody. Of course, he got good publicity and saved the registration fee for himself. Neither Vinobha Bhave nor his entourage ever trust the officials who know the procedure inside out; and Bhave's ignorant committees of distribution are composed of donors themselves. We haven't achieved anything like what we claim, but it needs an expert to drag the truth out of a tangle of statistics.

'Those poor devils of officials at the village level', he continued, 'have to produce figures for the wonderful reports compiled at Headquarters. They have to show how many improved chulas were built during a month; whether people actually use the chulas is no concern of theirs. Of course, they invent figures to justify their existence. Take the Cottage Industries Centre. What is really important is how many of the trainees are able to use the new techniques; but what counts for statistics is the number trained. Whether they were able to make any practical use of the training, whether the articles they produced had a market, is irrelevant. I'm sorry for them.

'As for the senior officials, a Deputy Collector is zealous, over-zealous indeed, until he is selected for the Administrative Service. Once he becomes one of the Heaven-born and his pro-

* Acharya Vinobha Bhave.

motion is assured, he becomes either a political tight-rope dancer trying to keep himself on the right side of every faction, or a glorified Babu simply following a routine. These fellows work in blinkers; no one knows what the rest are doing. There is no idealism urging everyone to work. The present-day official just marks time.'

I was asked to address the villagers before I left Venkatapur. I talked to them of the old days, of the troubled times the village had passed through and how the Government was doing its best to help them. I told them of the challenges they had to face and the great efforts needed of them. I ended up by saying how glad I was to see their school, particularly when the number of pupils had gone up six-fold during the last ten years. I said it was only through education that they could make a success of democracy. 'If you don't educate your son', I said to the Harijan member of the Panchayat, 'he can become only a chaprasi (office messenger).'

'Not at all', gently muttered Narsing Rao, 'he may become a Minister', a remark not unexpected from a person in the opposition.

The day I was leaving Venkatapur amidst touching farewells, Ranga Rao, an old friend of Rihaz's and mine, suddenly arrived. It was a pleasure to see him. He appeared to have changed in many ways, although I found he was still conservative in his thinking and orthodox in his beliefs. In the intervening years he had enjoyed a quieter life, had read a great deal and seemed reconciled to the thought that his own generation had no part to play in the shaping of things. We talked of Rihaz and the interlude of storm and stress, of Mallaraju and that lucky escapade, of Vasanth Rao and Aggi Reddi and of the changes that had taken place during the last eventful years.

'Although we're still a poor country, things *are* better in many ways. The old peace has returned to the land; the lawlessness and violence that we knew immediately before and following independence has disappeared.'

'At least the Government is making a terriffic effort', I said. 'The country is humming like a dynamo.'

'Oh yes, the Government is trying to do its best, but the most dangerous moment for an indifferent Government comes when it begins to reform itself. Perhaps we are passing through that moment.' He looked at me through his thick glasses like an earnest, pedagogic bird. 'What can a Government do, with the best will in the world, if the human material is not there? Where is the toughness, the sense of duty and dedication, the singleness of purpose we need? We have no real national consciousness, no will to work, and yet we talk about socialism as if it were a magic "open sesame"! Tell me, how can we have socialism without hard work?'

'I'll be humble before the immensity of the task', I said with some weariness. 'But look at the tremendous advances the country has made during the last ten years; perhaps the very fact that many people today are conscious of shortcomings does show a real awakening. What is ten years in the life of a nation, with so much ignorance, superstition, tradition and outworn ways?'

Ranga Rao smiled, showing his white row of teeth. 'Well! We certainly have things on the credit side too. We are making an omelette, of a sort, but I'm sorry for the broken eggs!'

Ranga Rao had come to ask me to attend the wedding of his seven-year-old daughter. The formal invitation was printed on glossy yellow paper, the corners of which had been dabbed with turmeric and kum kum powder. It was customary to use these to attract good luck and as an auspicious gesture a handful of coloured rice was also given to me. The wedding ceremony was to be at three o'clock in the morning. Ranga Rao explained that the hour was determined by astrologers after studying the horoscopes of both the bride and the groom.

Ranga Rao was enlightened enough to oppose early marriages, but pressure from his grandmother had left him with no choice even in the case of his own child.

I started for Ranga Rao's village after dinner, along with Narsing Rao and a few others; we travelled by jeep and, on reaching the village, could easily find our destination by following the sound of music from the Shehnai. The Shehnai is an ancient musical instrument played by mouth, and, in most parts of India, is a sign of special rejoicing. Of course, as in most cases, the absolute opposite can also be found. There are communities that play this music at funerals. Death to them is the great redemption from the fall that was life.

We were heartily welcomed by Ranga Rao and his family. Fresh mango leaves hung in a row on the doorway and elaborate designs had been made with rice flour on the floor. The house, like all rural houses of the well-to-do, was like a small mud fortress. The front door opened into a large quadrangle. A dim, religious light inside was given by numerous little earthen cups, geometrically placed all over the ground, in which burned cotton wicks soaking in sweet oil.

We hurriedly crossed the quadrangle and joined the other guests. Ranga Rao sat next to me to explain the details of the ceremonies. He himself was a Brahmin and therefore a member of the elite. The priest who was to conduct the ceremony, though not a Brahmin, occupied nevertheless a niche a little higher, for he alone could preside over such occasions. No matter where one attends a wedding of this kind, this ubiquitous priest seems inevitable, and no matter how humble he is in his profession, he is sure to be fat, pot-bellied and only half clad. This one wore nothing but a loin-cloth, more transparent than muslin, through which gleamed his dark skin. Every few minutes he took generous helpings of snuff, then shook his fingers violently.

In the centre of the quadrangle was a small canopy made of palmyra leaves and freshly uprooted plantain trees. The bride and groom were to sit beneath it for the religious ceremony.

The groom, a boy of twelve, and his bride, a girl of seven, were carried to the wedding place in wicker baskets. Each was borne by two half-clad Brahmins. The bridal couple were dressed in garments which had been soaked in turmeric water to give them a yellow colour. The feet and hands of the bride were also painted yellow with turmeric, and complicated designs had been made with red kum kum paste on her feet. They were escorted into the mandapam (canopy) from opposite sides, while a curtain held up by two Brahmins divided them.

At this stage, the bridegroom appeared to rebel. With umbrella in hand, he threatened to walk away. I asked Ranga Rao what it all meant. He explained that it was a customary mock show. The bridegroom was pretending to go away to Benares to live the life of a Brahmachari or ascetic. Ranga Rao now joined in the act. He interceded and requested the boy to reconsider his 'terrible' decision. To make the reconsideration worth while he offered his daughter in marriage.

The groom was made to sit on one side of the curtain, flanked by his parents and relatives in their gorgeous clothes. Likewise, on the other side sat the bride and her parents.

The elaborate ritual began as the Purohit started reciting hymns in a monotonous tone and a burdensome 'Savadhana sumuhurdha Savadhana . . .'. He was joined in chorus by a few others who sat behind him. They were the uninvited Purohits and Brahmins who always gate-crashed at such functions, knowing full well that for their efforts they would get, if nothing else, a good meal and the customary dakshina (gift).

All this time, the Shehnai continued playing, accompanied by a drum. The music now worked up to a crescendo. I realised that the moment must be of some dramatic significance and craned my neck over the squatting gathering to get a better look. Ah, yes! The bridegroom and bride were placing a piece of gur (unrefined sugar made from palmyra juice) on each other's heads; the dividing curtain was removed, and the little girl looked upon her playmate of yesterday with innocent wonder and unconcern. Then, through a golden ring fixed to a yoke, water was allowed to drip on her head. This was to drive away the evil influence of unseen spirits. The Purohit was now chanting more fiercely than ever.

Meanwhile, I observed a priest moving among the women and carrying something in his hand. This was the thali (a small hollow golden talisman), tied to a string of black beads which was to be fastened round the neck of the bride by the groom, the final seal to the marriage. The music blared forth more violently as the Brahmin tied the thali round the bride's neck, and the privileged women (the mother, aunts and elder sisters of the bridegroom) sat behind the bride to make sure that the knot was securely tied. It had to be knotted thrice; neither more nor less. As each knot was tied the guests tossed handfuls of rice on the couple to bless them.

And now, tied together by the hems of their garments, they walked round the sacrificial fire, tracing the traditional seven steps round the flames to the old Vedic ritual. This done, the marriage was sealed and the two children became man and wife. A yoke was placed on the necks of the husband and wife as they walked a few paces, symbolising the fact that they were now bearing a common burden and treading the same path with a common goal.

What followed was not part of the actual marriage. It was only a homa, a sacrificial offering made by the new couple to their gods for long life and prosperity. For this, the sacrificial fire was again lit at the centre of the canopy. It was kindled with wooden sticks and fed from time to time with melted butter.

How omnipresent is this fire in the Hindu ritual! Whether it be a wedding or a funeral, a christening or an anniversary, a fire must always burn; the fire that consumes all yet illumines all, as the silent witness, an eternal seal of all Hindu consecrations.

The bridal couple did not understand anything of what was said, but dutifully added the melted butter to the fire when directed to. Many pleasant ceremonies followed, like the throwing of flowers at each other.

At the completion of the ceremonies there was the inevitable feasting on a lavish scale, ending up with the distribution to the guests of betel leaves and nuts and a large coconut accompanied by the sprinkling of rosewater from a silver holder.

For quite a while I thought of this wedding. With the impact of modern education, the custom of early marriages in South India is fast dying out, yet the grip of tradition is still so strong that even college-educated fathers find it difficult to break loose.

And so I took my leave of Venkatapur and the little world Rihaz had known and returned once again to the great world outside. From the plane that evening, India far below looked wrinkled and brown in the gathering dusk, with occasional patches of dull green. I could see nothing of the roads, the wells, the terraces and irrigation reservoirs upon which were labouring some whom I knew and a vast army of anonymous workers. From far away, progress is measured in statistics which have been filtered through many layers of officialdom ... not by a clean water-supply here, an improved variety of cotton there. But there is gain in having a bird's eye, as well as a worm's eye view. Down below progress may often be imperceptible; from day to day, month to month, nothing much seems to change and a man loses hope. From up above, if setbacks and failures are blurred, the general trend is visible. Progress there is; the poor may still be poor, but they have more than hope to sustain them. The leaders, with all their faults, are learning, even from their mistakes.

What we were witnessing is only the beginning. The people are being roused, and their destiny is passing into their own hands. Rihaz would have understood this; it is what he himself would have wished. If this tale sets down the strains, the stresses and the tragedies through which the countryside he loved was fated to pass, it is also the record of his confidence in the capacity and the will of the people to leave the dusk behind and to climb the heights over which the dawn is surely breaking.

Glossary

Achkan, formal dress coat with high collar
Anna, a small coin, now obsolete, worth about one penny
Badmash, a villain
Bania, trading caste, popularly associated with money-lending
Begar, forced labour service
Betel, the leaf of the *betel* tree, chewed with the dried areca nut as *pan*
Bidi, coarse country cigarette
Chowdi, (*chawadi*), 'a place where four roads meet', a hall or shed used as a travellers' resting place and also for the transaction of local affairs
Chula, cooking place of clay
Churidar, tight, pyjama-style trousers
Dak bungalow, formerly a rest-house for those who carried the post by road (literally, *dak* means 'post')
Dallam, a Communist cell or fighting unit
Daya, a midwife
Deshmukh, 'head of the country'; in medieval, Hindu times, hereditary district officers; then landlords
Devdi, mansion or palace
Dhal, a porridge made of split peas or pulse
Dhed, one of the three main Untouchable castes of South India; their quarter is the *Dhedwada*
Durra, 'master, sir', title of affectionate respect for official or man of education
Ghair mulki, person who does not belong to the State; not of the country
Girdawara, middle-rank district revenue official
Gunta, one fortieth of an acre
Guru, religious mentor
Gutka, porridge, made of *Jawar* (qv.)

Gutta durralu, 'Masters of the hills'; term here given to the Communists

Holi, the Hindu saturnalia; marks the start of the hot weather

Inam, a grant of land in perpetuity

Jagir, also a land grant, usually for services rendered; the holder is a *Jagirdar*

Jawar, (*juar*), millet or barley grown on non-irrigated land

Jungli, of the jungle or forest; wild, primitive

Kavalkar, hereditary village watchman

Koya, aboriginal hill tribe

Maisamma, Goddess of Smallpox

Moharrum, period of fasting and mourning for death of Hassan and Hussain (AD 669 and 680)

Namaste, Indian salutation with pressed palms

Neem twig, the *neem* tree has a bitter sap which is said to be a disinfectant

Pan, a green leaf which, with a little *chunnam ketetchu* and *betel* nut, is chewed by many in India and South Asia; when chewed it tints the lips and teeth red

Panchanama, a deposition

Panchayat, council or committee of a village or a caste

Paratas, wheat bread fried in butter

Patel, hereditary village headman

Pattadar, a registered landholder

Patwari, hereditary village accountant and keeper of the revenue records

Rupee, coin worth about 1s. 6d. or twenty-one US cents

Sadhu, a mendicant

Sarkar, 'government', title of respect accorded to high officials

Sehra, a fringe of flowers

Seth, a businessman, owner, master

Sufi, a mystic

Taccavi loan, a small loan to support the agriculturist

Talukdar, from Arabic *'alak*, 'to hang, or depend'; has many shades of meaning, but in the context of this book means the District Officer

Tehsildar, the chief revenue officer of the *Tehsil*, a sub-division of the District

Toddy, a corruption of Hindi *tari*; the fermented sap of the *tar* or palmyra tree

Tonga, a pony-drawn carriage

Yetti, forced labour (cf. *begar*)

Zamindar, 'lord of the land', owner of an estate